# PHOTO, PHYTO, PROTO, NITRO

# MELISSA MCCARTHY

Sagging
Meniscus

Set in Mrs Eaves with LaTeX.

ISBN: 978-1-952386-65-7 (paperback)
ISBN: 978-1-952386-66-4 (ebook)
Library of Congress Control Number: 2023937220

Sagging Meniscus Press
Montclair, New Jersey
saggingmeniscus.com

*If your 20-year-old self could see you now, what would he think?*

That I should have thought a little more about my choice of tattoos.

—Dave Grohl, musician, *Financial Times Magazine*, 30/31 January 2021

# Contents

# *Illustrations*

# PHOTO, PHYTO, PROTO, NITRO

# FLOWERS

## *phyto*

*Phuton* is "that which grows; a plant," and *phyto* (the *u* sharpening to give a "fie" sound) is the prefix that indicates a relation to plants. As in *phytography*, the description of plants, and *phytographer*, an expert in or writer on this field. There's also *phytoscopic*, caused by the sight of them. If, for example, seeing a flower makes you vomit, then it has had a phytoscopic effect on you. (Although the word is more commonly used to describe the situation when a caterpillar changes colour to match the surrounding vegetation.)

## Tatts and time

My mental response, particularly to tattoos that I don't like, is, 'That'll never come off, you know." I changed my thoughts, or perhaps my perspective, on this, when last year I saw a surfing/literary contact sharing online images of her large, back-covering tatts of delicate cherry blossom, along with a comment to the effect that the ink was only as permanent as the span of her remaining, already adult, life. Looked at one way, the indelible markings, like the blossom, and the person, are transient. It depends on how you are conceiving of time.

At around the same time that I saw this Japanese-influenced decoration, I was reading *Hiroshima*, John Hersey's long reportage on the bombing. The *New Yorker* magazine received his piece and decided, for the first time, to dedicate the whole of one issue to the story, rather than serializing it. Thirty thousand words appeared on 31$^{st}$ August 1946, with Penguin in the UK bringing out the text as a book the same year. In it, Hersey finds and follows the stories of six residents of the city, tracking each person from their position on the morning of 6$^{th}$ August 1945 through the course of their day, and the aftermath.

It's a strange book, detached in tone, giving each character's details without particularly entering into their internal worlds or their feelings. The story builds as Hersey combines his six witnesses' accounts in a cubist manner, presenting all these from his later, researcher's vantage point. He ends with a description of one son's nightmares, drawing attention to the child's unsophisticated, surface interpretation of events. But part of the book's power lies in the fact that everyone's reactions and interpretations were unsophisticated, utterly uncomprehending. His characters do not know what in the world has just happened to them. They are left, leaderless, to wander round the devastated city, with only rumour and visceral experience to guide them.

And no-one, faced with this new, unleashed weaponry, is entirely sure what's happening. The U.S. has the technology to inflict the bombing. But with the first atomic weapon testing having taken place less than a month before, there are gaps in their knowledge, too. Hersey explains, "Long before the American public had been told, most of the scientists and lots of non-scientists in Japan" knew the details of the bombs. While such information was still subject to security in the U.S., Japanese scientists marshaled their knowledge and had it "printed and mimeographed and bound into little books," which circulated and proliferated. That's a volume I would be interested in seeing: a samizdat atom bomb explainer in Japanese.

I'd picked up Hersey's book in the second-hand bookshop, hoping that it might contain information on an aspect of the story that I was vaguely aware of. This is, the idea that the bomb blast had caused some sort of photographic imaging onto the very concrete of the city, that a shadow-puppet picture of Hiroshima at the moment of its annihilation remained. And his book does mention this, but not exactly as I expected. Hersey explains that the story I was looking for was just that, an urban, or urban destruction, myth. The bomb had indeed been so bright that in some places it had illuminated an object and at the same time caused the shadow that this object cast to remain marked on the ground. "A few vague human silhuettes were found, and these gave rise to stories that eventually included fancy and precise details," such as that a shadow image persisted, fixed onto a wall, of a painter dipping his brush into a paint can; or the dark outline of a cart man about to whip his horse. But these are just "one story [. . .] another," says Hersey. It's not as true as had been rumoured, that the atom bomb inflicted this uncanny form of photography. There's a gap, between the story of the image, and the real markings made by light.

## Bluets and bayonets

Hersey gives more credence to another form of marking, though, when he describes some of the dreadful injuries among survivors: "the burns had made patterns—of undershirt straps and suspenders, and, on the skin of some women (since white repelled the heat from the bomb and dark clothes absorbed it and conducted it to the skin), the shapes of flowers they had had on their kimonos."

Hersey's book is shocking not just in these awful details, but by his very calmness, his ability to tell the story in measured, sober words. This happened, these people made it through that day and the subsequent ones, they could tell their accounts. Life went on. And we keep reading. The setting, the city, began its regrowth immediately, as Hersey reports:

> Weeds already hid the ashes, and wild flowers were in bloom among the city's bones. Everywhere were bluets and Spanish bayonets, goose-foot, morning glories and day lilies, the hairy-fruited bean, purslane and clotbur and sesame and panic grass and feverfew. [. . .] It actually seemed as if a load of sickle-senna seed had been dropped along with the bomb.

## On flower with corpses

With this destruction, and strange flowering, Hersey is in a good literary tradition. Aeschylus, in his *Agamemnon*, written in the fifth century BC, has the sea flowering with the corpses of men. What's this war reportage that Aeschylus is making an artwork out of; what's the story? The Greeks have won the war at Troy, at last, by means of their secret, innovative equipment, and can finally leave the war zone. Agamemnon, king of Argos and leader of all the Greeks, is coming home, preceded by a herald who brings the news. The audience sees this herald telling the Argive chorus that

Photogenic drawing of a hornbeam leaf by W. H. F. Talbot, England, 1840.

The grey diagonal line—historian Larry Schaaf calls it "the footprint of a slash"—stems from the way this image was arranged in the Bright family album, marked by the notches used for slotting in pictures. The pale splotches are not from excess light but from the glue used to stick the drawing onto the page.

although Agamemnon is indeed just on his way, there were problems for the rest of his army: many of them, after enduring all the troubles at Troy, were nonetheless drowned in a huge storm which struck the returning flotilla. The herald's own ship survived, and in the morning he surveyed the damage. He reports this in a sentence (lines 658–660) that has been variously translated over the last couple of hundred years. Here are four versions of it:

J. S. Blackie, 1850:

> And when the shining sun
> Shone forth again, we see the Ægean tide
> Strewn with the purple blossoms of the dead,
> And wrecks of shattered ships.

Robert Browning, 1889:

> And, when returned the brilliant light of Helios
> We view the Aigaian sea on flower with corpses
> Of men Achaian and with naval ravage.

Anna Swanwick, 1886:

> And when uprose the sun's fair light, behold,
> The Ægean sea with flowerage overstrewn,—
> Corpses of Grecian men and wrecks of ships.

Philip Vellacott, 1956:

> The bright sun beamed—we saw
> The Aegean flowering thick with faces of dead Greeks
> And scraps of wrecks.

Because the sentence has such imagery, and such translations, I went to look at the original ancient Greek text. There are two particular words from the lines that interest me: *anthoun*, which means "flourishing" and is the word that tells what state the

Aegean sea was in; and *ereipiois*, "wreckages," one of the items connected to this flourishing (in Greek, ἀνθοῦν and ἐρειπίοις). It takes a bit of construing, here. But just cling onto the ideas, of *anthoun* and *ereipiois*, flowering and wrecks, as I'll be returning to those.

The skeleton, framework, of the sentence is: in the morning light we saw the Aegean sea. What was the sea doing? It was *anthoun*, "flourishing, abounding." And it was abounding with two things: wreckages (*ereipiois*) of a nautical sort, and corpses (*nekrois*). Corpses are easy. Wreckage, rather more complex.

*Ereipiois*, the wreckages, is a form of the noun that means "a fallen ruin, a wreck," and it derives from the verb *ereipo*, which has a broader set of meanings. It can be an active verb, to throw or dash down, to cast down (as in, "some God casts them down," Sophocles, *Antigone*, line 596). It can be passive: for a wall to be thrown down, or for thunder to be hurled down by Zeus. Then, it can be an intransitive verb, with no object, particularly in Homer's *Iliad*: a warrior falls to his knees; a tree falls from its root. There are no cases in the lexicon about flowers scattering and falling, ruined, from the tree. Thinking of a Japanese haiku school of poetry, one might expect to see fallen petals as a sign of mortality. But that doesn't seem to happen in the Greek.

So the implications of *ereipo*, verb and associated noun, are of ruins less delicate than blossoms: fallen buildings, wrecked soldiers, blasted trees. And all these types of ruin can be found, they coincide, in the flotsam described by Agamemnon's herald. (Flotsam: wreckage found floating, while jetsam is goods thrown overboard [or, jettisoned], that then might be washed ashore.) He's talking of planks, which were trees, before their felling, and then were the dwellings and vehicles of men; now they are broken, cast-down bits, next to the corpses. The word, along with the scene the herald describes, is a confluence of references and allusions.

Then, the straightforward meaning of the herald's word *an-thoun* is that the sea was blooming. It's the participle of the verb meaning "to blossom or bloom, to be bright." What is the herald describing? An expanse of water, with dead bodies rising up all over the surface, in the same way that flowers poke up their colourful heads all over a meadow. But strangely it's a word that is also used "of the youthful beard," referring, I guess, to how the new stubble pokes through the skin of a man's face. And to the "bloom of youth"—all ideas of freshness, new growth, a pretty appearance that attests to health and attractiveness, vitality.

In a slightly less concrete sense, the verb *antheo* also means "to flourish, thrive, be at the pitch or full extent." The dead Achaeans (=Greeks) are, some of them, young men who are finally victorious in Troy: they are flourishing, until a sudden reversal of fortune. Then they re-bloom like flowers, in this awful necronautical inversion of the metaphor.

It's a dense sentence from Aeschylus' herald, but a good one, moving in word order from "morning" to "we saw" to "blossoming" to "wrecks." End on a downer. It's something I'm going to trace in this book: newness, vision, flowers, blasted trees. Proto, photo, phyto, nitro.

## Under the stones, the sand

Writing earlier than Hersey in *Hiroshima*, but not by much, is another man who's trying to establish a record of what went on in the past. What civilization was there and what violence; what happened to the people.

It's the British archaeologist Leonard Woolley, writing two Penguin books on his excavations at Ur. This is, the home of the biblical Abraham (the proto-patriarch), in southern Mesopotamia, where the Sumerian civilization ebbed and flowed over several millennia. In 1854 the British Museum, noting bumps and traces under the desert, supported some investigation for a couple of years, and round the turn of the century, more preliminary work was undertaken. Then a vexing want of pence, explains Woolley, delayed the diggings, but in 1922 he was appointed director of a new Joint Expedition (with the University of Pennsylvania), and the results were spectacular: tombs, grave treasures, temples including the Great Ziggurat. From the layout of a whole city down to the smallest earring, Woolley and his teams unearthed a vast amount of material. But as he's at pains to point out, the objects, though magnificent in themselves, are only the means through which one can understand the structure, habits, and beliefs of the past, can make it coherent.

And the method? He dug down, sinking great shafts, and noted how the items that he found varied according to position: something deeper than something else would usually be older. A grave underneath another must have been put there first; pottery from layers below would be of an older style. And underlying all this was a huge stratum of fine river mud, giving solid—mud-solid—proof of the biblical flood. In a pre-carbon dating era, none of the discoveries gave proof of absolute ages. What the layers over layers did give, however, is a sense of sequence; they allowed Woolley to calibrate different eras, to understand how they aligned with or succeeded others. At the simple end of the scale this might be done by seeing how the design of burnt bricks changed, as new residents with new cultural influences arrived in the area. Sometimes more sophisticated items of comparison were used, such as temple records that listed the figures in a dynasty and gave dates, which allowed for matching against other sources of information.

I like this indication from Woolley on how to proceed: dig down, arrange your items, even if they appear to be in an unlikely location, then examine, compare, and match them until you can build a wider understanding. Until you can see the whole field, work out where you're standing.

## On air

In his generalist book *Digging up the Past* (1930), Woolley gives a brief overview as to the why and how of archaeology, and explains that sudden destruction (as from a "conveniently adjacent volcano," or, failing that, from sacking and burning) is good, because it preserves so well. There is also much to learn from slower methods, the gradual accretion of time, rubbish, land. Even if people take no deliberate action towards a site, it will not remain as it was; by-products or side-results of their other activity will still have an impact, and nature will do its thing, too.

Plants in particular carry out this work of preserving, and Woolley gives the example of a central London site:

> I remember how, when the L.C.C. cleared the slum area where Bush House stands to-day, the heaps of broken brickwork and loose mortar were in the following year entirely hidden by a mass of purple willow-herb, and people used to take bus rides down the Strand just for the pleasure of looking over the high hoarding at this miracle of wild flowers. That happened in the space of a few months; had the 'island site' been left undisturbed for as many years, coarse turf would have covered the mounds and the ruins of Booksellers' Row would have been buried like those of Silchester. And if this can happen in the heart of London, how much more so in the country, where Nature fights at close range?

(The L.C.C. is the London County Council, the metropolitan authority at the time, and Silchester is a preserved Roman camp, in Hampshire.) It's a nice image from Woolley. One would think that he mentions Bush House because of its radio connection, its fame as the home of the B.B.C.'s World Service, as his book is based on a series of six talks that he gave for the B.B.C. But this isn't, in fact, the prompt: *Digging up the Past* was written in 1930, well before the transmitters were ever there, on the rubble-and-flowers site. Construction on BVSH HOVSE, as its portico carving proclaims itself, began in 1925 and lasted a decade; it wasn't until 1940 that the B.B.C. set up camp there, only removing in 2012. And the name doesn't derive from plant-loving, (or, shrub-happy, phytophilous) builders, but from the American industrialist Irving T. Bush, whose project it was. So it wasn't transmission of radio waves over the air that drew Woolley's attention to Bush House, but the seeds of plants, disseminated over the building sites of London on the breeze (or deposited there by birds), re-establishing their hold.

## Her ribbons and her bows have fallen

In his other popularizing book on the excavations, *Ur of the Chaldees* (1929), Woolley talks about the discovery and deciphering of the Great Death Pit (up until him still unplundered), which held scores of royal attendants, neatly reclining, among the most splendid treasure. Some of the magnificent costumes and ornaments were still there, preserved, on the queen and her retinue. There were shells used as containers for cosmetic powders, jewellery, haircombs decorated with golden beech leaves and flowers. Almost half the women had hair-ribbons of gold; the rest had none. But then Woolley made a deduction; from discolouration of the bones, he grew certain that the women without gold ribbons had instead had silver ones: "there may be detected on the bone of the skull slight traces of a purplish colour which is silver chloride in a minutely powdered state: we could be certain that the ribbons were worn, but we could not produce material evidence of them."

Among the finery, the ropes and ribbons of gold and stones, there should have been silver ribbon, but it had rotted away. Woolley then finds a proof of this, beyond the purple traces. In an example of little human foibles reaching a finger through five thousand years to brush us on the face, Woolley found that one of the maids still had her silver ribbon coiled up in its case, presumably because she was late getting ready, and had to rush out of her dressing room before having time to tie it in place round her forehead. So it stayed in the case like camera film left in the reel, and, unexposed to the atmosphere, did not have a chance to decay, like those of the better-prepared maids.

That's what we can see through Woolley's century-ago eyes: the purple tinge of where silver used to be, on the body of the women. A blue-ish marking, a decoration, a faint, permanent tattoo. An adornment that has lasted far longer than the person.

## Royal blue, permanent

Woolley himself is touchingly amazed at the persistence of objects through time. And, more liminally, at the persistence of traces, visual images of objects. He talks us through the process of digging, explaining that sometimes "a paper-thin wavy line of white powder" can be seen in the earth, and this is the edge-on sight of a reed mat used to wrap a body. It's astonishing, he says, that

> a fragile thing like a piece of matting, though it lose all its substance and can be blown away with a breath, yet retains its appearance and texture and can with care be exposed in such condition that a photograph of it looks like one of the real matting which perished 4500 years ago. So too with wood; nothing of it survives, but on the soil there is left an impression, a cast as it were, which with its effect of grain and colour might deceive the eye, though a touch of a finger obliterates it more easily than it dislodges the plumage from the wing of a butterfly.

The image remains, although it's utterly fragile. And a photo of the image can't be distinguished from a photo of the item. It's almost holographic: when we dig, we can see the grave-mat, its grain, texture, colour, but it can be squandered, by the archaeologist simply breathing, by a touch. I love the way he brings in the butterfly wing, too, with its structure of light-processing, its colours. Later I'll consider photographer Emmet Gowin taking pictures of moths and their traces through the night, after he's spent a little too much time with nuclear explosions. Things being blown away, and an image remains, only just.

Woolley lived in a more formal age than mine (he was born in 1880), and he can be seen in three portraits (as well as in various digging-site photographs), two of which are held by England's National Portrait Gallery, and one by the Science and Society Picture Library. It's the same face in all three, unmistakably, with a similar expression, same smartness of suit, same pose. But one, the latest, is taken by Walter Stoneman in 1954, not so long before Woolley's death in 1960; he's about seventy-three. A middle portrait, by Bassano Ltd., is taken in 1938. He looks slightly harsher, a bit vulpine. The third portrait is unspecified, listed as circa 1930. The placing of his head, the pyramid-esque eyebrows, the uneven hooding of one eye, the neatly curving mouth—these are carbon-copy similar to the 1938 picture. But though the exterior is the same, there's something different about his emotion: he's indefinably younger, more beautiful, less stern.

## What's below this field of vision?

Something hard to notice or articulate under the surface? This is the very province of archaeology. And interpreting the image by studying its surface: this is how we look at photographs. The two activities combine in the practice of photoclinometry, which is, studying aerial photos so that differences in light and shadow can reveal information about the below-ground. For early-twentieth-century archaeologists, the aeroplane was obviously a great new tool for this, but as Woolley explains in *Digging up the Past*, even standing on a hill at the right time of morning or evening, with a sloping sunlight, can give the archaeologist a clearer picture of where to dig, thanks to faint shadows indicating irregularities, unflatness, in the plain or plane of vision. Brick structures below the earth provide an easier path for plant roots to wriggle through as they seek out the dark and nourishment, giving bushier outcropping above ground. You can even, says Woolley, detect what's waiting underground by perceiving, "in the very early morning, a difference of tone given by the dew on the blades." That's a beautiful way to start the day, looking for history in the reflection of sunlight off the water droplets.

So this is what Woolley does; he examines and interprets the field below him, then he digs down and goes through the layers, comparing bricks, bones, silver, texts, and temple stones. He's trying to line up the various things that he finds, literally when he's working out what depth of digging matches what other finds, figuratively when establishing the relations between, say, a particular style of pottery and a reign, a date range, a culture.

This is what I want to do, too: hold items from different levels beside each other and establish a timing and a meaning for them, set them on a wider flood plain. I plan to align some texts and artifacts and work out what they might indicate about culture. It might seem that the juxtaposition is wrong, that something from one era could not possibly cast light on another item. But archaeology allows us to see many levels at once, and photographs, in particular, make it easy to shift in time, to juxtapose and arrange the layers differently. As with Woolley's photos, I always find it moving to see pictures of one person at different times, as they glide on through. Like the attendant with her silver ribbon, Woolley's traces remain. He's been caught there by the silver halide crystals, held on the paper.

## X-rays

Back to Hiroshima in 1945, where the profusion of flowers over the debris is like Woolley's Bush House willow-herb. Back with the ruins and the dead, displaced, and "doomed" people. Hersey uses this last adjective in an interesting, old-school way, meaning something I'm not quite sure of, something around being cursed, or condemned to suffering. Doomed in that an awful blow was coming upon them and has come? Or that many will surely soon die from radiation poisoning? It was the case that some of the damage instigated by the blasts could not be seen at the time; it was hidden mutation, causing sickness and death as time went on, as the sores refused to heal.

What had caused all this? A *hanakago*, or flower basket, suggests someone in Hersey's account, meaning, some sort of cluster bomb. But it's worse than this. Through one of Hersey's protagonists, a doctor, we learn that,

> Word went around among the staff that there must have been something peculiar about the great bomb, because on the second day the vice-chief of the hospital went down in the basement to the vault where the x-ray plates were stored and found the whole stock exposed as they lay.

Of course there was something peculiar: the radiation from the atom bombs. Later in the hospital they burnt bodies, carefully putting the ashes into envelopes that were meant for the storage of X-ray plates after they'd been exposed. Each one was labeled with a name, and they were piled in one office. "In a few days, the envelopes filled one whole side of the impromptu shrine." It's hard to comprehend the scale of the event, even reduced in this way to one small element of it, in one office, of one hospital. It was people's bodies in the envelopes that had been meant for X-rays; a substitution of flesh for image, but flesh that's been exposed to too much light.

## Yucca, Shoshone, Skull Mountains

Spoiled X-ray plates appear in another time and place, also in the realm of atomic weapons. It's the work of Emmet Gowin, an American photographer born in 1941. In 1996 he finally obtained permission to fly over the Nevada Test Site, in airspace controlled jointly by the U.S. Department of Energy and the Air Force. This is one of the places where the government carried out experiments into the use of nuclear explosions, detonating bombs both above and below ground. Robert Oppenheimer first used the atomic bomb in New Mexico, in 1945; in Nevada, tests took place from 1951 to 1992.

Gowin presents the photos he made in 1996 and 1997 in a 2019 book, *The Nevada Test Site* (from Princeton University Press), with an essay at the end explaining the slow unfolding of his project. It's all breathtaking, just the scale of what happened, how much power. And the number of explosions—"test grounds" doesn't seem the appropriate phrase. A test implies that you're trying to find something out, make a discovery, check something. If even the very first explosion showed the awesome power of the weapon, and two deployments of the nuclear bomb showed how effective it was in practice, why, one wonders, were over a thousand more detonations needed; how much could be enough. It seems like the military were showing, if not to the enemy, as extensive secrecy and security is still in place, then to themselves, that they did indeed have this power; they were not testing but proving grounds, the site of display of their horrifying, absurd strength. (And in fact that was the name prior to 1955—the Nevada Proving Grounds. It's now known officially as the Nevada National Security Site, or NNSS. I like the duplication.)

## The image seen by the unarmed eye

There's one detail in Gowin's essay, a conversation he has with a pilot, which burns into the page.

> One mind-bending story was about a batch of Eastman Kodak X-ray film that was worth, perhaps, millions of dollars. As soon as the film was made, it was tested and found to be mysteriously spoiled from exposure. This batch of film, even after repeated testing, proved a total loss. In trying to discover what had happened, Kodak eventually approached the Department of Energy and asked, "Is there any way that radioactivity from one of your tests could have reached the eastern United States? Could radioactivity released into the atmosphere reach the southeast?" In the pilot's story, that's what seems to have happened. Radioactive dust and debris from Nevada had entered the jet stream and been carried east over the American South. A rainstorm dumped that radiation onto cotton fields. When the cotton was picked, carried to Rochester, turned into cellulose acetate (film base), and coated with X-ray emulsion, it was sufficiently radioactive to expose and ruin the freshly coated film.

After I first read this in Gowin's book, I misremembered it as applying to normal, snapshot film, so that hundreds of holiday photos would have come back ruined, the memories of a happy time all blurred and bleached by some indirect nuclear age contamination. But it makes more sense that it is the base of the X-ray film that caused trouble, by the mutancy, the radioactivity embedded within it. X-ray film is meant to depict what is not visible to the doctor's eye: the bone behind the skin, that which is hidden and buried inside the body. But in this case it is within the very substance of the image that we find the power, the abnormality, which impacts on the emulsion. It's like cutting off the tree branch that you're sitting on; the film spoils itself. It never came to the point of being used in the medical setting, never got as far as disturbing the view of someone's bones; during testing it was apparent that this film was already damaged and could not be used.

This project of Gowin's is an attempt at holding to account, making sure that these huge, repeated actions should not be forgotten. It's the same, in some ways, with Hersey. He also wants to present the dreadful facts, to bear witness, by preserving and presenting how his six characters experienced the events of the days. It's a way to bring to light and to record the memory. They are both in the context of bombs, and of pain. And they both bring in strange images of flowers and growth: Gowin with his damaged cotton, Hersey with the rampant weeds, the kimono burn patterns, the hanakago. There are flowers of destruction, and flowers of persistence, memory, keeping the trace. I see similar strands in another form of writing, and this is the memory book.

## Palely loitering

I need to make a leap here, from the American journalist John Hersey writing about Japan in the 1940s, to his compatriot Peter Benchley, writing about East Coast U.S.A. in the '70s. There's a character in Benchley's 1974 best-selling novel *Jaws*, a story of a shark bothering a beach town one summer, who might have slipped the memory of most readers. It's Patrolman Len Hendricks, one of the more minor figures, both of the book and of director Steven Spielberg's film *Jaws* of the following year. But there are some points about him that are worth picking up on, from among the pages.

It is Hendricks who is unlucky enough to witness the third shark attack. He reports to his boss, Police Chief Brody, "That's the biggest fuckin' fish I ever saw in my whole life, big as a fuckin' station wagon. I went in up to my waist and tried to get to the guy, but the fish kept hitting him."

Then Hendricks grabs the victim's arm in order to pull him ashore, but it breaks off in his hand, as the body has been so savaged. Hendricks, notes the local newspaper the *Amity Leader*, "by

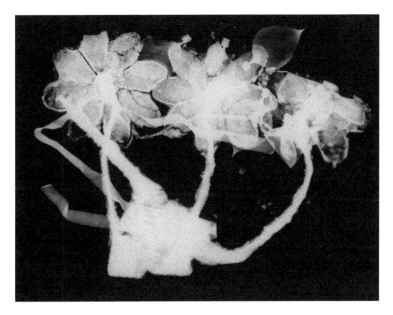

X-ray of a wax package containing a gold head-dress decorated with flower shapes and a silver comb, from Ur, third millennium BC.

Archaeologist Leonard Woolley's team began excavating the tombs in 1922. The British Museum registered possession of the package—to the naked eye it looks like a clump of pebble-encrusted dirt—in 1929. Then there was a delay until 2002, when the museum radiographed the item to provide this image.

sheer coincidence was taking his first swim in five years." It's also Len Hendricks, on a gory streak, who discovers Chrissie Watkins, the first victim of the shark attacks. He sees part of her body snarled up in weed and kelp: "The mass of tattered flesh was a mottled blue-grey, and as Hendricks spilled his guts into the sand, he thought— and the thought made him retch again—that the woman's remaining breast looked as flat as a flower pressed in a memory book."

Len is a Vietnam vet and a pulp fiction fan—he's reading *Deadly, I'm Yours* when the first missing person call comes in—so it's perhaps surprising that the image that comes to his mind as he vomits is this rather archaic one.

## Do not forget, that wherever I am I remember you yet

Memory books, autograph albums, repositories for collecting messages from friends, still existed in the early 1970s, as they do today, but it's not their heyday. They were used by schoolgirls in the early twentieth century, and by male university students through the nineteenth, but their roots lie in the *stammbuch* or *album amicorum*, which is, a book which you invite your friends (*amici*) or your tribe (*stamm*; your crew, posse, your intellectual circle) to inscribe you a message in. It's a trend that took hold in German universities around the mid-sixteenth century. This was an era of wandering scholarship: a young man would travel between institutions both within Germany and internationally, and the stammbuch was a way of maintaining a thread of continuity, a permanent record that offered proof of where he'd gone, whom he had met. It reminds me of the memory-prompting function of tattoos on sailors: a memento of each important place or sweetheart on his travels. In blue ink. And it functions, too, as a sort of proto-photo album.

At each institute, the student would ask eminent teachers, social superiors, and his own peers to sign their names and write messages, which were often learned quotations in various lan-

guages. Or a contributor might put in a coat of arms, or an illustration. A book might contain only blank pages, for the signator
to inscribe at will. But some albums interleaved these with wood-
cut illustrations, or with pages taken from an emblem book, which
is another sixteenth-century phenomenon: a collection of instruc-
tive, illustrated morals in verse. Let's step back to browse it.

## Start with the splashing ducks

Among emblem books, at the bottom of the pile (chronologically
speaking), we find the Italian Andrea Alciato, with the first version of his *Emblemata* appearing in 1531 in Latin, while for a first
work in English we have Thomas Palmer's *Two Hundred Poosees* of
1566. (Palmer's "Poosee" is an alternative spelling of "poesy," used
from the fourteenth century as an equivalent of "poetry" in general. A poesy or posy can also be, specifically, a short motto, then a
gathered set of poems. And, parallel to this last meaning, from the
sixteenth century onwards it's the name for a nosegay: a bunch of
flowers, not poems.) Palmer's book is followed by many others, including the fabulous *A Collection of Emblemes, Ancient and Modern* of
George Wither, in 1635.

Those are some of the prototypes. What's the format? In appearance, an emblem book usually gives a page to each concept,
with an *inscriptio* (short motto) at the top, then a *pictura* (picture),
and a *subscriptio* (longer, verse text). So, to pick an example from
Wither from among his four hundred (Book 3, no. 23), the inscriptio is:

> Through many spaces, Time doth run
> And, endeth, where it first begun.

Under this is the pictura, a circular engraving of a happy woodland scene, ducks paddling about in front of one bare-branch tree
and a leafy woodland. Behind the pond there's a building (chapel,

mausoleum, a bush house?) of some sort, and in the foreground but framing the edifice in a perfect circle is a snake eating its own tail. Also within the snake-loop, free-floating, is the word in Greek, "eniautos," which means "a cycle," specifically in the context of time and years. In the border of the pictura is the phrase "in se sua per vestigia volvitur," which is from Virgil's *Georgics* (Book 2, line 402): "The year is ever turning around in the same footsteps." And under the image is the subscriptio, a thirty-line poem about changing seasons, the *ouroboros* figure, and the inexpressible nature of eternity. This is what an emblem is for: to illustrate, with allusive detail, a thought. The various parts of the emblem work together, but they also add an interesting tension: the motto isn't telling us exactly the same as the image, nor yet the verse. And there are words in the picture. It's a more multi-vocal, complex form than might appear. It's a genre well ready for a come-back, I think.

The printed emblem book stood alone as a hugely popular format. But it also began to merge into the stammbuch, in that people would ask friends to add a signature to their personal copy of an emblem book. Conversely, they would cut out particular pages from an emblem book and stick them within a stammbuch, as a prompt for a contributor to respond to. The emblem book led to the stammbuch, and the very similar autograph album, which in turn developed into all later memory books. There's a common concept: written messages of friendship, plus drawings, or perhaps small objects.

One of the most notable, and oldest, examples of an album is held at Pembroke College, Cambridge. It's the *Album Amicorum* of cartographer and scholar Abraham Ortelius, with contributions dating from 1574 and continuing until probably 1596, two years before his death. Some of the pages of Ortelius' book were offered blank, for his friends to fill in. Some of the pages already had images on. In this case, however, they were not extracts from an emblem book; not poem and picture, but frames. There are forty-five pages of these ready-made spaces. They all feature *trompe l'oeil* decoration in blue ink, with blank cartouches, roundels, and boxes surrounded by elaborate borders, bolstered with statues, vases, human figures, scrolls. Each page is a visual representation of the trappings of a painting, with an empty centre circle inviting a drawing, while text boxes above and below provide a space for the written message. Instead of pushing ready words, the Ortelius templates offer decorative zones in which to write and draw, blue ink frames for the images still to come.

## Remembering, dismembering

Ortelius' book, while rather short on flowers, does have around one hundred and fifty contributions, of which my favourite is from one Georg Braun. It's an example of these template pages, ready-drawn in blue, waiting to be filled in, which Braun does using brown ink. His contribution is: dismembered body parts, specifically two hands, on the ocean floor. They are lying over two side-by-side creatures: a lobster and a snake whose tail is knotted. That's the picture: snake, lobster, hand, hand. In the central circle with them, written inside the circumference, is the motto, advocating moderation: *Nec laxa, nec stringe*. Which means, neither relax nor draw tight. Don't: extend, lighten, weaken, loosen; draw tight, press together, squeeze.

In the lower text-box is a friendly message from Braun to Ortelius, and in the top rectangle/plinth is the headline text of the piece, *moderata durant*, meaning, things in moderation last, or, with moderation, things persist. It's a motto based on the words of (again) Agamemnon, in Seneca's *Troades*, where he says "Ungoverned power no one can long retain; controlled, it lasts" (line 259, translated by Frank Justus Miller, Loeb, 1917). He's talking about what it is permissible to inflict on the conquered people of Troy, when the wheel of fortune has spun in one's favour. It's right to act within bounds, observing moderation. Not taking to extremes.

So putting together the whole of this page, what's the combined message? Power exercised in moderation can be held onto longer. But, when you have hands, don't grip too tightly, nor release too much. As illustrated by this animal-grabbing fable of the snake, lobster, and downfall.

I've got to say, this is not ringing any bells. Is the message that a lobster pinches too tightly with its claws, a snake does not surround something closely enough with the coils of its body, and as a result, a person has their hands chopped off? It could allude, suggests art historian Alexia Shaw, to some moral about the surrounds of the creatures themselves: a lobster has a tight, hard carapace, while the snake's skin is exceedingly flexible, and in the end just sloughs right off; it doesn't hold tightly to the flesh. Or the instructions concerning holding might apply to the activity of the human, who could transport a dangerous creature, but only by holding it just right. Too loose a grip, and the snake will be able to squirm round and bite you. Too tight, and you'll agitate the lobster and it will pinch you.

It looks like they are on the sea bed, but this might just be suggested by the presence of the lobster. They are in front of a small hillock or peak. Has the lobster with its claws, and perhaps the constricting action of the snake, cut off the hands, one each? Has another character amputated them? Are they Agamemnon's sailors, lost at sea on the way home from Troy? What's going on, with these body parts on the sandy floor?

## Prefiguring

I've been scouring the emblem books for clues as to what might have inspired Braun's message to Ortelius, and though some of them do feature snakes or lobsters, I haven't found this exact scene. There is marriage guidance in Alciato's *Emblemata*, in the example of the sexually-aroused viper courting an eel (it's a moray). There is in Wither's *Collection of Emblemes* a lobster squashed under a globe, giving us the message that, "The motion of the world today / Is moved the quite contrary way," much as a crab doesn't advance straight. Wither also gives us an image of an un-excised hand grasping a snake: "However thou the viper take / A dangerous hazard thou dost make." Then he lists various situations in which it's unwise to get involved: don't listen if your friend is talking treason; don't get between a husband and wife when they argue; don't fall for someone who just won't love you. Don't do it, not to any extent. Coming from the hands angle, the closest image is of a hand emerging from a cloud, whose outstretched finger is being nipped by a snake, with the sentiment from the letters of Saint Paul, asking, who is against us? No lobsters.

There are these examples, and a few more, but nothing as specific, nothing that would inform Georg Braun's strange imagery. The only circumstance that I can think of that would explain it is that Patrolman Len Hendricks has been there. As he says of the victim whose death he witnesses, "I took hold of one of his arms and pulled. [. . .] It came off in my hand. The fish must have chewed right through it, all but a little bit of skin." That's who provides dead human hands on the sea floor: Hendricks and a great white shark. Hendricks pulls off the hands, then in his alarm drops them, and they float on down to the sea floor and rest next to the denizens there. The shark could circle round and come back up Amity beach to resume its dinner, if it wanted. A main (or *main*) course.

That's the rationale I propose for Braun's lobster-snake-hands in the blue-ink framing of Ortelius' album: that he's pre-empting Hendricks' failed rescue attempt in *Jaws*, by showing a body dismembered, un-armed, by a shark. He's drawing a picture of the horrifying scene that Len will encounter in the 1970s, several layers up in the strata of time and books. And flipping the line of sight in the mirror, bouncing back through time, Hendricks in turn thinks back to the stammbuch, when he sees, on the mottled blue-grey of Chrissie, the first victim,'s body, something like a flower on a page of the memory book.

But this is absurd, of course; it would require time to have got mixed up, looped around, in order for a modern-day patrolman to be influencing the image in Ortelius' book of the late-sixteenth century. And the reverse: absurd for the idea of the autograph book to be influencing Hendricks' thoughts, as he unearths a body. But that's what we have.

Through many spaces time doth run, and, like Leonard Woolley matching up his figures from many different layers of the dug-up past, we, too, can shuffle around the items, seeing what lines up. From my perspective, I can put them all in the frame. I have the pleasure, and the privilege, of time.

### Ribbon, reason

It's a strange image for Len to turn to. He's walking in *Jaws* the book along the very waterline, when he sees Chrissie's body tangled in the seaweed, her body which has been washed back onto dry land, out of the ocean. She is presumably drenched, waterlogged. But he sees her breast as like a dried flower in a book; a way of preserving the flower, retaining information.

There's an important strand in *Jaws* (both of them) about record-keeping: what does the coroner agree to understand and classify Chrissie's and the other deaths as; what will go down in the official record; what do the newspapers hold back from printing about the incidents? In the film we are shown Police Chief Brody poring over library books about sharks; and there is a super, under-appreciated scene of Brody typing up documentation on death.

The camera shows us a busy, troubled Brody at his office desk, in front of his typewriter. Then the shot changes to a close-up, from his point of view. We can see just how close the camera has come, the level of zooming in, because conveniently this shot is of the central, business zone of a typewriter, which has a measuring bar all across it. (Typewriters terminology alert! Paper rest, carriage return, roller knob, ribbon spool, platen, guide, paper fingers, strikers, escapement. Touch selector.) I think it's the paper guide, with rulers, that I'm referring to, here. In Brody's case, it's a thin, metal bar marked in red with numbers, from twenty on the left, then ten, zero in the middle, then counting up again towards the right. The red of the numbers and the calibration lines between them are matched by a swoop of red typewriter ribbon that looms up from the bottom of the image before retreating into shadow, over on the left. Everything else on the screen is black and white. (I wonder if Leonard Woolley saw the Sumerian coiled silver ribbon in its case and noted any similarity to typewriter ribbon. After all, Woolley and Brody are engaged in comparable activities: looking at the spooled ribbon to make interpretations about death.)

## Spell it out

The silver metal bar holds the paper behind it, so that it doesn't flop forwards over the keys. And the bar's markings show the scale of the paper: this shot is an image (to be projected onto a screen ten, twenty, forty feet wide) of six inches of real space. It's a small expanse that shows a surprisingly wide range of information, as the paper on which Brody is typing is the death report on Chrissie Watkins. It's a pre-printed page, with regions that need to be filled in for all sorts of details. (In this, it's like the blue drawn cartouches of Ortelius' *Album Amicorum*—the ready page, the empty spaces.)

Some of the field titles we can infer by the answers that are visible, the replies that Brody has already typed: occupation of victim, date and time of incident, current location of body. Then the scene shows Brody hesitating as he comes to type in the box labeled "probable cause of death." He doesn't want to say the answer. But he has to admit it, one somber click at a time: the cause is "S H A R K."

This is good, but even better, though, is the very next box over from "cause," which asks for "reason." No wonder Brody looks so perplexed at his task. How can we separate cause from reason; what's the difference? They are both factors that precede an event; they are things that make something happen. I pondered this for a long while, before wondering whether there is an element of proximity: perhaps "cause" is what immediately leads to the event, while "reason" is a more remote part of the same process? In this case it would mean that time was a vital ingredient: cause is now, reason was back then. There don't seem to be hard and fast rules on this. And then the scene, and Brody's report, muddy the waters even further by showing that there is a clarification, written after the all-caps REASON, in smaller, minuscule letters. The form is asking for "REASON: quarrel—illness—revenge etc." Brilliant suggestions—these do all seem to be events, states, proximate situations that might lead quickly on to death, though I'd have thought they'd be in the "cause" section. But I'm not the Amity public records office.

I feel that Brody has been sent here straight into a Greek tragedy sense of causation, of why does anything happen. In tragedy, the answer's probably: yes, all of quarrel, illness, revenge; these are the reason. But there's always something else behind. Why was Agamemnon (after the herald's harbingering) killed on his return to Argos? Because he had sacrificed his daughter, left her dead on the water's edge. Why had he killed his daughter?

Because there was no wind, but he had promised to lead the expedition to Troy. Why did he have to do that? Because Paris had stolen Helen. Why? Because he'd been sent out to reclaim Hesione. Why was she there? Because of the voracious sea creature. Why? Because before. Why? Because. It's strictly in time, and with a delay: everything has happened already that will make this come to pass. Like taking a photo: why will we have it? We will have it because of what's been put in the wooden box before, and we will have it only after a delay. Maritime violence might well be involved.

Brody struggles with the difference between what's the cause and what's the reason, and really, it's a difficult question. For him (and in the real 1916 East Coast shark attacks that heavily inform the action in *Jaws*) there isn't actually a reason: just one of those shark years. It came along, and now he has to deal with it. Or possibly: Brody has a shark problem because of the *auctor ex machina*: Peter Benchley needs there to be a shark so he can construct a conflict, make a story. Or: Brody has a shark problem in order to create a book about home and belonging, the interloper into the community; about exogamy and hospitality; Hooper's overreach and nemesis; everyone's growing understanding that decisions have repercussions: *Jaws* is a Greek tragedy kind of book.

## Long time ago

Are flowers just records or markers of death? It's not quite that. They do appear in the same arena as places where there is death, and there are records being made. Hendricks' mental image is that the body looks like a flower. But this body then sets off contention, about correct or false textual recording, and it leads to Brody's philosophical quandary of reason versus cause. All these elements are caught up in the same nexus, of flowers, bodies, reported information, attempts to establish a written record that will retain the knowledge, that will assist us in forming the memory. It's a nexus that John Hersey would recognize.

After Alciato's text-and-image pages, memory books did start to incorporate items, such as an embroidered scene, a lock of hair, or a pressed flower. It's easy to spot the symbolic value of such a flower in a memory book: there's the implicit comparison between the flower and the young person, particularly if it's a teenage girl's book: the metaphor of a girl flowering (like the herald's sea, *anthoun*, flowering) into sexual ripeness is a well-trodden one. But the ephemerality is built into the image; flowers don't last long. And there's an internal contradiction in the fact that a pressed flower has had all the liquid extracted, but instead of killing it, this allows the flower to be preserved indefinitely. It's in a zombie mid-state, never quite dying, but no longer alive. The book, for its part, is more long-lasting than the organic matter pressed within it. That's why it is used; to maintain the image, the meaning of the flower, to share with it the persistence of the book. But there's a contradiction here, too: books themselves are notoriously fragile; they're also made of organic matter, just in more processed form. They are still destroyable, by bookworm, moisture, neglect, fire. That's why we keep them in solid stone libraries. Which themselves are apt to fall into ruin, be burned down, or be smothered by a convenient volcano, to Leonard Woolley's delight. As he says, the ruins of Booksellers' Row would soon be covered by turf. Everything becomes the ruins, though along slightly different timescales. It'll all end up among the *ereipiois*, the wreckage. On which will grow the flowers.

## Herbarium

There's another locus where flowers are pressed on cardboard, ready for perusal, and that is the herbarium, the perfect meeting place of paper and plant. Luca Ghini and Gherardo Cibo, working in Bologna and Pisa in the first half of the sixteenth century, began the practice of preserving flowers by pressing them between sheets of paper until all the moisture had gone. (The herbarium is the term for both the immediate collection of preserved plants, and the broader institution of learning around the collection.)

Before this, flower collectors and herbalists used paintings and drawings to share information on the medical properties of plants, from Discorides in the first century up to John Gerard and others in the sixteenth century. There was a change of emphasis with voyages to the New World; the collections of Joseph Banks, then later Hans Sloane, William Dampier et al. were gathered with an eye to the commercial exploitation of these resources. Picking flowers, when examined through a lens of colonial exploitation, becomes a far from harmless pursuit. There's a reminder of this in the fact that the Biblioteca Angelica in Rome, which holds the Cibo herbarium of 1532, illustrates this collection on their website with a pressed poppy—the flower whose product has caused perhaps the most strife of any. Although the tulip might put in a claim for contributing to economic chaos, at times. Or rubber, palm for palm oil, sugar cane—the list of candidates proliferates.

What's the purpose of a herbarium? It allows researchers now and in the future to observe the size, shape, and structure of the plant. Each sample is carefully labeled as to its colour (in case it fades), and with where it was found. This allows the tracking of plant distribution, to see if changes in climate, or human activity, or anything else, might affect where the plant can thrive. A use that wasn't originally envisioned is that scientists can now take DNA samples from old herbarium sheets, and trace familial development and variation. There's also the idea of one example of a particular flower acting as the "type" or "voucher specimen," the sort of ur-flower that others can be compared against. The proto-poppy. The herbarium itself is of a family with the fungarium and the seed bank; with the palnyotheque, which holds spore from ferns, and pollen; and with other libraries and collections of material; in it, one can trace the development of Linnaean classification, of modern science, in action.

And for fans of the recursive, I note that just as a herbarium is a collection of flower samples, so too do herbaria themselves become grouped, organized, collected, at the *Index Herbariorum* of New York's Steere Herbarium. Actively managed, accessible, permanent scientific repositories from around the world are the items that the *Index* gathers; it's a catalogue of plant collections. Like a dictionary collects words, or a zoo collects animals, or a museum, photographs. That's the basics of the herbarium, from Cibo's prototype to the present.

# Early Processes

*proto*

The prefix *proto* indicates that something is primitive, an early attempt, the original, whether that's of a language, a design, or a creature. It can indicate pre-eminence, as in a *proto-forester*, the chief among woodmen, or it can show shared descent, as in the *protastacus*, the common ancestor of all lobsters and crayfish.

In chemistry, *proto* in a substance name designates that the first and essential part is combined into a larger whole. In bibliography, the *protocol* is the first item stuck into a book (like a book plate is glued in) giving instructions on how all the following will go.

*Proto* is about starting a new thing.

## Botany with AA

There's this long, historical trail of images, then, stretching from the illustration of the flower to the pressed specimen, as used to assist in the study and cataloguing of plants. Then, at a particular nineteenth-century point in technological development, a new method starts to flourish: it's photography, with all of its cognates and associates. This doesn't seem to have affected the herbaria as much as I would expect; they kept on with their physical holdings of actual plants. But for books and illustrations, photography had a huge impact. I'll consider here some aspects of its early days, from around circa 1839, explaining a selection of the processes, the underlying concepts, and the substances that were put to use.

One of the practitioners or artists who worked at this juncture, moving along the tideline between old methods and new ones, was for a long time left in the shadows (or shallows) and is only in the past four decades re-emerging to prominence. This is Anna Atkins, with her *Photographs of British Algae: Cyanotype Impressions*, begun in 1843. *British Algae* was followed in the 1850s by a second work made with another Anna, Anna Dixon, which is *British and Foreign Flowering Plants and Ferns*; there is first algae, then flowers.

"Flower" is a scientific term, the part of the plant that contains the mechanisms for reproduction. It's also the group of plants that reproduce in this way, as opposed to, for example, conifers, which contain their seeds within cones rather than flowers. Algae are outwith this; the word is an expansive description for a broad group of plants that stretches from seaweeds at the large, complex end of the scale to weird, basic bacteria at the other. There is huge variety, within the fluid taxonomy of the plant kingdom. But flowers and seaweeds are both *phutons*, things that grow, of a similar scale. And away from the science, they overlap, in functional and art representation terms. People admire them as they stroll along, sometimes even eat them. You can use certain seaweeds on the garden, as a fertilizer. And what is it that flourishes along the tide-line? Certain shore-friendly flowers, like the silver-blue sea holly, but also seaweeds; those are the most common plants at the shore.

Early-photographic historian Professor Larry Schaaf led the way in the Atkins resurgence, with his 1979 article "The First Photographically Printed and Illustrated Book" (in *The Papers of the Bibliographical Society of America*). He then brought out two collections of her work and co-curated the 2018 New York Public Library Atkins exhibition, complete with a retail, facsimile edition of *British Algae*.

Schaaf distinguishes that Atkins' *British Algae* was not a private album circulated among friends but a proper book, "a formally issued work [. . . distributed. . .] at her own expense to a number of institutional and personal libraries." He explains that it came out in serial, in rather protean fashion, between October 1843 and September 1853. Thirteen initial parts combined with later sections to form an eventual three volumes, each containing up to 411 plates, in addition to text pages with intro, dedication, and contents. Schaaf examined seven versions of the work that have survived, in whole or in part, out of the "at least ten and probably more" that were originally made. He explains Atkins' position within the photographic coteries of the era—she corresponded with both scientific polymath Sir John Herschel and photographic pioneer William Henry Fox Talbot—and discusses her use of the technology.

## A wooden box, with holes in it

To set Atkins' work in the context of early photography, it will help if I explain some of the terminology and techniques that were swirling around in the photographic waters at this point, near the end of the 1830s.

If the question was, how can we retain an image after the real thing has gone, the answers arrived via various paths, sometimes confusingly entwined. The early methods did, however, share a conceptual underpinning, that light effects chemical changes on a treated surface, changes that can be preserved.

In 1839 in France, Louis Daguerre publicized his eponymous daguerreotype, made by using mercury fumes to fix an image onto a silver-plated sheet of metal. In England, Talbot, in contrast, worked on paper. His first works were photogenic drawings, in which specially treated, salted paper is exposed to light until a negative image appears on it, and this image is then stabilized. The image in a photogenic drawing might be caused by the rays gathered by a lens after they bounce off an object at a distance. Or, in the case of the even more simple photogram, an object itself—a leaf, a bit of lace—was placed on the salted paper and this presence was what caused a differential in the light reaching the paper. From these paper negatives, a reversed, positive print could be made: what many of us would think of as a proper photo. After the photogram, Talbot devised the calotype, another sort of negative on paper that could be used, in turn, to make positive prints.

Some photographs were obtained using a piece of equipment that is familiar to the late-twentieth-century viewer: a camera, which is, a wooden box with a small hole that allows the light to enter in particular quantities, usually through a lens. But a camera was not necessary for all forms of photography; some, like the photogram, only required an item to be placed directly onto the treated, receptive paper. This was essential; there's no photography without the surface.

All of this undergoes an alteration, through time: what we're familiar with, the tools we use, what qualifies as a photo. For a younger reader, this would be the digital image on the computer and phone screen. But at the start of the grand chemical age of the form, a metal or paper surface treated (brushed, soaked, dabbed) with substances was the site of the photograph.

## Delta blues

Atkins herself used the particular process of the cyanotype, which is a sort of photogenic drawing, no camera needed. Invented by Herschel in 1842, the cyanotype's distinctive feature is its rich, blue colour, created by the iron present in the chemical mixture with which the paper is brushed. When exposed to light, this ferric content reduces and reacts, becoming a bright, Prussian blue which is insoluble in water.

So Atkins' method was to take her piece of seaweed, place it on paper treated in this way, press it down under glass, and expose it to the light. Where the substance of the seaweed blocks the path of the light, the chemicals on the paper are hidden and do not respond. Where there is no seaweed, the light can hit the paper unimpeded and cause its chemicals to react and change colour. After a few minutes an image of the shape round the seaweed starts to appear; the paper is then washed in water, which halts further change in the exposed chemicals and washes away the unexposed ones. Hang it up to dry and you are left with a permanent, negative picture of wavy, white seaweed drifting in the deep, iron-based blue.

Why blue? Because that's the colour of the substance that reacts in this way (ammonium ferric citrate mixed with potassium ferricyanide). But it's a fitting colour, beyond just the chemical; fitting for the subject. Atkins' cyanotypes are negative images: what our human eyes, if we were in the room with her, would originally see as a dark seaweed laid against white paper, in her presentation becomes a white blot against the blue, and we, perhaps unconsciously, make the link with the submarine. Each of her seaweed pictures is, for the viewer, a shape floating in the blue, just as, we know, the sample before she gathered it was also a shape floating in the blue of the water.

But there's something about the Atkins cyanotypes that place them in a liminal position, strangely at the delta. They are remarkably accurate depictions of the specimens, but they look like... well, what? Like everything. Browsing the collection, we can see intricate, branching shapes to her seaweeds, like the complex networks of neural connections in the brain, the routes through which electricity, ideas, and memories run. There's one among her images that just matches the weeds of the famous shot in *The Night of the Hunter* (director, Charles Laughton, 1955), when Shelley Winters' character is dead underwater, in the car, her hair waving and the long weeds flagging around her. (Though this is black and white.) The blue of the cyanotypes also looks like blue skies, with white clouds. Atkins would be familiar with looking at clouds. But to me, the straighter lines in her images look like aeroplane contrails, the lines that follow planes through the blue sky. This was not a visual experience Atkins herself could have had. But how we see is cultural, contextual. Some images become, if not icons, then containers of much more meaning.

Not long after the 11th September attacks on New York in 2001, I saw a collection of photos from around the world, made by various photographers, anywhere. I remember this newspaper double-spread very clearly, and I keep searching for the set of images. But I can't find them anywhere. They showed: a chalk drawing on the yard floor, scrawled by children as they played under drying sheets on the line. A chunky graphic drawn on the four thousand-pixel screen of the simple mobile phones that existed then. A graffito on the wall. More. The thing that the pictures had in common was that they all showed some representation of two tall rectangles and a diagonal cross shape approaching them: all pictures of the Twin Towers and the planes on the way to explode them.

Now, when I see Atkins' white, puffy lines against a clear blue background, I think, these are plane trails, but I see no planes;

where are they? Everyone knows where the planes have gone. The building that was there has turned into dust. Things that didn't seem fragile are suddenly easily destroyed, after all.

Or to offer a different context, and a different way of seeing: Amsterdam's Rijksmuseum included Atkins' cyanotypes in a 2017 exhibition, following their acquisition of one volume of *British Algae*. Schaaf's *Talbot Catalogue Raisonné Blog* includes an installation view taken during his visit to this exhibition, showing copies of 306 (all but one) of the images, tiled out on the wall, in nine rows of thirty-four columns. It's suddenly clear, in this image from the Dutch museum, what the blue of the cyanotypes is like: blue delft tiles. What we see is shaped by what we have already seen, what we think should be there, in that particular place.

## Tentacles and tinctures

Atkins' work garners increasing appreciation, and the cyanotype process has been revisited by various artists throughout the twentieth century, at intervals. It never went away as a tool for architecture, as it's the method used to make blueprint drawings, a stage on the way to constructing a dwelling. In 2008 the artist Christian Marclay worked with the cyanotype, making images of cassette tapes, unspooled so that they trail loops of magnetic tape like a jellyfish trailing its tentacles, through the blue background water. These cassettes are recording and playback technologies, usually for music. I note that Marclay's other concern, much more famously in his twenty-four hour piece *The Clock* from 2010, is time.

In another context but also with a musical link, the neurologist Oliver Sacks, in the *New York Times* of 20th August 2012, writes about searching for the perfect blue. It's not just the drugs talking. Sacks, being desirous to see a true indigo colour from among the whole spectrum, sets himself up with:

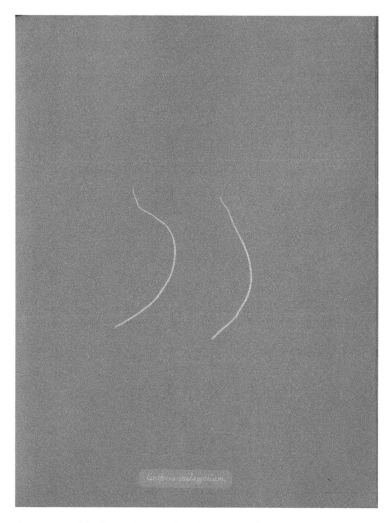

A cyanotype of *Conferva melagonium* from *Photographs of British Algae* by Anna Atkins, England, c. 1843–1853.

Alongside the melagonium are other conferva with great specific epithets, or, second halves of their scientific names: arcta, albini, Brownii, diffusa, fontinalis, implexa, Linosa, polita.

a base of amphetamine (for general arousal), LSD (for hallucinogenic intensity), and a touch of cannabis (for a little added delirium).

And it works:

> there appeared a huge, trembling, pear-shaped blob of the purest indigo. Luminous, numinous, it filled me with rapture: it was the color of heaven, the color, I thought, that Giotto spent a lifetime trying to get but never achieved [. . . ] the color of the Paleozoic sea, the color the ocean used to be.

Then it disappears, this vision in blue, until one day the following year, when Sacks is at the Metropolitan Museum of Art listening to a Monteverdi concert. In the interval, he wanders out into the Egyptian galleries, and sees hints of indigo in the rocks and jewels. The music has brought it back to him, rewound to a connection, re-enabled his vision. And then it goes, and he never encounters the colour again. Is this tragic, to think that not only might something as tangible as a building, a tower'd citadel, smash, but something as elusive as a colour, too? Even the blue is as contingent, fleeting, as vanishing as a drug-enabled linkage in the brain; things are easily lost.

## Mostly nameless colours, colours you'd like to see

The cyanotype is a sort of photogram, which is the method where you place an object on the paper to obtain an image of it; Atkins used seaweeds. There is another picture from the same era of a similar watery object, made using the same method. This is a salted paper negative of a shark egg case, or, mermaid's purse, taken circa 1840–1845 (it's from the Gilman Paper Company collection, now in the Metropolitan Museum of Art, and it was found in an album associated with the Bright family of Bristol. The actual creator of the negative has not yet been pinned down). It's a lovely image of the case; that is, a container for future life that floats in the fluid of the sea, just waiting. (I'll be discussing a little more about the body of the shark, below. Don't worry. I was coming to that.)

This image of the mermaid's purse is a photogram rather than specifically a cyanotype because the chemicals are different, using silver nitrate rather than an iron-related substance on the paper. But the process, and the concept, are the same: the treated paper reacts to the extent it is exposed to light, and can then be fixed with this negative image in place where the item has blocked the access of light to the surface. The result is a pale brown object on a darker brown background—again, it's a negative. The solid, pale body of the case contrasts with the fine, spiraling tendrils that spin out into the dark space around it.

Though the cyanotype was ideal for Atkins' purposes, it was soon superseded by incoming methods. Photography went one route, with Talbot himself in 1844, a year after the commencement of *British Algae*, sending subscribers the first installment of *The Pencil of Nature*, a collection of calotype prints (and one negative) on salted paper. Representation of plant samples mainly went in a different direction. In the 1850s, nature printing came to the fore, a process in which a plant was squashed into metal, which was electrotyped—precisely duplicated in copper—to produce a plate that could then print out repeated copies. The example that Schaaf footnotes is Johnstone and Croall's *The Nature-Printed British Sea-weeds* of 1859–60. These are also beautiful images, with their branching and blotching, although they are somewhat shocking to a reader immersed in the Atkins cyanotypes, because the delicate seaweeds are illustrated (in three respective volumes) in brown, red, and green ink against a buff background. Out of the blue, we're suddenly into a new zone of plant imaging.

## Nothing new, under the sun

New ideas kept surfacing in the photography world. In the 1850s Louis Désiré Blanquart-Évrard introduced multiple printing onto albumen-treated paper, and Frederick Scott Archer introduced the wet collodion process, to make negatives on glass plates; this was, in turn, mainly replaced by the more convenient dry plate method. An element that many of these ongoing methods had in common was silver: the daguerreotype, the calotype and the collodion negative, non-cyanotype photograms, the salted paper positive print and the albumen print, and up to today's regular camera film; all these use silver-based compounds and chemicals, in place of the cyanotype's iron base. In the 1890s the Lumière brothers worked on the problem of how to obtain colour images, and by that time the whole issue of motion was raising its head, too. Then sound, digital, the whole nine yards.

One understanding of the story of photography allows for the new technology to enable a new way of seeing the world and representing it. But there are other influences on the art form, not just chem-tech innovations. Peter Galassi, for example, contends (in his 1981 MoMA exhibition and publication, *Before Photography: Painting and the Invention of Photography*,) that the development of photography in the 1830s was not a technological advance that allowed a new aesthetic to develop, but was, rather, coincidental to an artistic trajectory that was already underway. Painters were already moving from illustrating concepts to observing their surroundings; from expanding on a theme to abstracting a rectangle of tone, shape, colour; aiming for the dissociated, the fragmented, the optical. The image would no longer be ordered and given meaning by a religious, architectural, or social scaffolding; it would just be what the painter could, lens-like, see.

There are technological changes, but there are also tectonic shifts in how this art form is institutionalized and popularized; there is always the question of what photography *means*.

Present-day historian of science Peter Galison is another writer who usefully traces ideas of the progress of photography. He's no relation to Peter Galassi, curator at MoMA, but it's strange how names seem to echo and recur, faint repetitions like a blurry print. Galison traces scientific image-making through different stages: the ideal version, showing how scholars thought an item should be; then a mechanical, mimetic image showing the particular, singular version; then an image as considered and used by the expert practitioner; and now, not as something we look at but as part of a constantly feed-backing observation system, within which we function. From metaphysical to mechanical to interpreted to systems of control, as he describes it (at, for example, his lecture at Edinburgh College of Art on 25th September 2020). Galison also offers thoughtful discussion of black hole imagery (with Elizabeth Kessler in *Aperture*, 2000), and brings in Wittgenstein's discussion of the category of games, to suggest that "scientific image" is perhaps a better word than "photo," as our understanding of photography and image-making changes through time, and the category shifts and becomes fuzzy.

There are all of these directions, influences, trajectories, when we talk about photography. But there are some aspects that seem fundamental, including: proximity, light, and time.

## How close, how bright, how long

First, the question of proximity: what elements within the whole set-up are touching other elements, and what, in contrast, can happen at a physical distance. I've mentioned that the photogram involves putting the object on the paper, and this does not require a camera. In theory the object could be at a little distance from the receptive paper, but this would result in a more blurred image, as the object's impeding effect would be reduced by light getting in behind it. But in practice, the item touches the paper; they're contiguous.

The photogram is not, of course, a print in the sense that potato-printing moves paint from a dish onto a vegetable onto a paper. The (for example) fern does not transfer anything onto the negative; rather, it blocks the light from reaching some parts of it. It's a form of stencil, in that the surface that is physically covered is not marked by pigment. This pigment is not applied by touching, but is, rather, activated: the exposure to light makes the chemicals within the page change colour. (Although the chemicals were painted onto the paper as part of the preparation.) It's like pressing a flower, in that you have to have the actual item physically there within the recording system, laid against the paper, in order to make the image. The photogram contains presence and touch. It also requires the right amount of light to be welcomed onto the paper, and this is the next element of all photography: how much light?

The photographer can restrict and manipulate the light, primarily by using a camera, which excludes some light, but which focuses other particular beams by means of its lens. In this case, the object can be at a distance from the negative, and the light travels from one to the other. We're all used to this idea: you can take a photo of something that is *from* you. Not at any particular distance, just not so close as to be touching your recording material. We understand photography as a physical-distance medium, like drawing; they both allow for making an image of something not next to you, as long as the light rays carry from the item to the recording medium.

## Carriage return, escapement

There's another distinction to be made, concerning a distance in time rather than in space. In *'From today painting is dead': The Beginnings of Photography*, the catalogue of the Arts Council's 1972 exhibition in London, the curator D. B. Thomas raises the point that early daguerreotypes needed what seems to us to be an extended amount of time for the image to register. He describes what happens when elements of the photo were unable to stay in one place for all the length of time needed for the exposure: "occasionally a blur or a 'ghost' image suggested the presence of a stationary horse and carriage or a pedestrian. Clocks have hour hands only." Clocks and ghosts: I like this early clue that photography is going to mess with time, and with livingness.

Time is not only the province of photography. All other art forms have it built in too; they help to carry the past forwards. There is the length of time that it takes a person to move, mix up paint, carry the brush between canvas and palette, or to scrape out the rock, or manipulate whatever medium. And there is the length of time that the image, once made, remains, so it can be seen far into the future. But there's a particular way in which time is central to the activity of photography, and that is via something discovered separately by Talbot with his calotypes and by Daguerre: the phenomenon of the latent image.

To explain this, think again of the simple cyanotype process, where the action of the sunlight makes an image, visible to the human eye, appear on the paper, and when this has happened to sufficient extent, Atkins takes the plate out of the sunlight, washes it, enjoys her algae picture. This is a print-out process, where the image appears at the time of exposure. The great leap, the *ta-ding!* moment in photography, comes with the discovery or invention that the photographer might briefly expose the negative so that light causes changes on the treated surface, but these changes are not apparent until a further application of chemicals. At exposure the image has been *made*, on the negative, but it is not *made visible* until later. It's a latent, or, lying hidden, image.

Photography, beyond other arts, has this extra time lag, in the latency of the chemical reaction to the light falling on the paper. Light stimulates the chemicals of the receptive surface. And then, dramatically . . . nothing happens. You cannot see any change on the paper. It looks the same. You can carry it around, in its same old state, for years even, if necessary, or if you forget. The change, that the light has wrought on the photosensitive substance, just lurks there, waiting for the developing stage. And it's only at this point, with further chemicals applied to the surface, that it becomes visible to the human eye of the photographer. An image, at last, appears on the negative. You can see, now, again, the scene or object that was photographed.

## It's there but we do not know

What's so crucial about this lag? Not everything needs to be immediately visible to the human eye. The chemical change has taken place, it's just we didn't see it. It's not a matter of faith; photos don't appear because we believe they will. It's a scientific matter, one based on previous experience. We trust this process has taken place, and will cause a certain effect, because Herschel and the others worked out what was going on, how chemicals will react through time, in different combinations, and they showed every subsequent photographer that this would work. It's normal, explicable, observable. But it's still a bit magic.

Do this, wait through time, and only then do something else so a picture will come. There's no such thing as an instant photo; even the Polaroid has the mysterious cave of the camera's body doing the procedures, buzzing and humming until after the delay the picture rolls out. (And by my logic, the phone screen is not, then, taking a photo. It's doing something else with algorithms, coloured pixels. But not, quite, taking a photo.)

With the latent image, there is a stretch of time when the substance of the receptive surface has absorbed the light, has had a change worked upon it, but we can't see it. Each grain of chemical matter is incubating. And this time, this period of "dramatically, nothing happens," is something that greatly interests me. The time when we can't see what alterations, what mutations are underway, not until the picture shows us, later. It's an idea that looks back to the radiation sickness that Hersey tentatively described in *Hiroshima*, and one that I'll consider, below, with Kuchnow's shark experiments. What's the progression, what's the timing, the discontinuity; when are there lags, lacunae, and lacks of smoothness? How does time cause, then mess with, our eventual images? The 1972 catalogue *'From today. . .'* refers to a "ghost," meaning a figure whose outline is not distinct. Something or someone has evaded their strict demarcation in space, and appears as a pale smudge on the image. They've declined to be fixed. But "ghost" is a loaded word to use, referring to a person who should be dead and buried, filed away in the past, the envelope, the shrine. Instead this person has refused to remain in the correct sector of time; they persist, a white blur in the dark of night. Every photo has a ghost, though. Persisting like a photograph, which keeps the image present before us although the moment has gone.

## Amniotic

Time and waiting: I mentioned as an example of the photogram the early image of a shark egg case that was found in the Bright family album. I love this image because it's from sharks, and because it makes solid the connections between the activity of photography and the idea of biological gestation: process, development, all these words about the importance of time before a new life emerges. The egg, the waiting, the something that will emerge from its dark, watery case, emerging as the copy of the parent into the next generation.

It's not just me who has noticed this; accounts of Daguerre's new method also use a language of pregnancy. Bates Lowry and Isabel Barrett Lowry in *The Silver Canvas: Daguerreotype Masterpieces from the J. Paul Getty Museum* (Getty Publications, 1998) recount how Daguerre dramatically unveiled his methods in Paris in 1839. The scientist Donné was there at the presentation, and in the following day's newspaper he attempted to explain Daguerre's new process. The Lowrys write:

> Even Donné, after his scientific training, was led, after describing the first three steps of making a daguerreotype, to resort to a metaphor to explain the mystery of the process by saying it was as miraculous as the incubation of an egg which produces a live chick. He also poetically described the washing of the plate as a baptism of this new being resulting from human creation.

(He's Donné, but before I could get the keyboard going right, I kept thinking he was our metaphysical poet.) It's an extraordinary, lavish account of producing a photo, bringing in incubation, birth, baptism. Part of Daguerre's process involves, even, fuming the silver-plated copper sheet with mercury vapour, which brings to mind incense and church ritual. The finished picture is in two tones, light and dark, but depending on the viewer's line of sight, it can appear either as a positive or as a negative image. It's usually protected behind glass, as it is susceptible to touch and can be easily smudged. This idea comes up often, of a surface so delicate that the slightest finger-tip, perhaps even a breath, would efface the vision forever.

What is easily damaged? Daguerreotype surfaces, butterfly wings. Sumerian reed mats, things that crumble even while we try to consider them. Material that could be easily blown away. Tombs at Ur, piled up for a long time under all the countless other graves, under the wood which is now "a paper-thin film grained in white and grey which can be seen and photographed but which a breath will make to vanish," says Woolley. What is lost? Some of the original volumes of Anna Atkins' *Algae*. Sacks' indigo, intertwined as it is with his mind and his music. Seemingly solid towers are lost— not one, but two. A city, a civilization. Some of them we find again, we find them in the image. What disappears? Sea foam, shadows, people, time.

## All the condiments

Against all this evanescence, I was struck, when reading about the early days and discoveries of photography, by how much solidity, substance, and, bizarrely, food produce there is involved in the experiments. Now we think of the photograph as a screen-based image, non-tangible, part of virtual reality. (It's easy to ignore the offshore cables, the server farms and whirling fans of the machinery.) But anyone born pre-1980 will recall the sensation of holding a set of photos in your hand, fresh back from the chemist's shop, and maybe the smell of developing fluids which came off them. This applied to a greater extent at the start of the medium, when all was tactile, sticky; photography took up space immediately around the photographer and the subject. Donné used the simile of an egg and a chick, but in photography, this was not just an admiring metaphor. Actual stuff was needed to make a photograph: household goods, food, even the galls from oak trees in your stately grounds, for gallic acid. (There are flashbacks to this in an eco-conscious/retro movement of organic photography, today.) And particularly: eggs.

One of the most heavily used substances was the albumen from eggs (chicken, not shark): the proteinous solution of the egg white. Blanquart-Évrard's 1851 idea, which became all the rage for the carte-de-visite, required paper to be coated in salty albumen, then silver nitrate, before receiving the image. In 'From today...' Thomas explains:

> It was estimated [. . .] that six million whites of eggs were used annually in Britain to provide the albumen for photographic paper. After the introduction of the snapshot camera had caused a boom in photography, but before the bromide print had ousted albumen paper, the Dresden Albuminising Company used 60,000 eggs per day.

> At the photographic paper makers girls did nothing else all day but break eggs and separate the whites from the yolks. The frothy albumen was then treated with bromide or chloride and poured into shallow trays. The paper was floated on the surface of the liquid and then hung up to dry.

> Most albumen paper tended to be made at the time of year when eggs were cheap.

This is great—the production and the market for paper and photographic images depended on the laying cycle of the chicken. And other, unexpected materials were also used. Photographic historian Roger Taylor in *Impressed by Light: British Photographs from Paper Negatives, 1840-1860* (Metropolitan Museum of Art, 2007) lists "sugar, honey, and other culinary substances" as components, and Thomas in 'From today...' mentions "tea, coffee, beer, syrup," in the preparation of plates. Animal gelatin was used to size (treat) calotype paper in Britain; the French, for some fancy continental reason, favoured a less robust starch and resin mix. The Lumières and their contemporaries in France round the turn of the twentieth century investigated how layers of potato starch dyed green, violet, and orange might help to obtain colour images of a higher resolution, for a more precise image. The involvement of foodstuff is taken to its logical extreme by incorporating the mouth into the photographic process. Thomas summarises a description from 1857 of how to create a positive print on paper from a calotype negative: "The prints were fixed with hot hypo solution and then washed several times. The absence of a sweet taste in the washings was taken to indicate sufficient washing." Actually drink your material, to see if the image is ready.

It's just a coincidence of convenience, but when Roger Fenton went in 1855 to the Crimea, where he became by far the most famous of the war photographers, and honed his considerable artistic skill, he used a converted wine-merchant's van for his on-site studio. (His letters, available transcribed online via De Montfort University, are a treat. In number 5, from 15th March 1855 to his wife Grace, Fenton explains how he'd had "Photographic Van" written on the side, so people wouldn't bother them asking what that van was there for, but that just caused soldiers to knock on the door at all inconvenient times, wanting pictures made.) It's another connection to foodstuffs. Instead of bottles of wine, he had his trays of chemicals. Instead of delivering wooden boxes of booze, he was producing prints.

I like something about the organic nature of making these early images, about how to do technology through substance. It's only a step further to the Cronenbergian: what happens when you start to fiddle about with the messy, biological, wet substance of the living human, mixing it up with the creation of the image? Or maybe it doesn't require sci-fi thinking, and is as persistent and as simple as a family resemblance through generations. When did you sit for a proper portrait, asked a friend of mine as she visited me at my parents' house. No, I told her, that's a picture of my grandmother; I look like her. Same picture, different flesh. It strikes me now, too, that I'm older than her, in the portrait. Time's gone tangled, again.

## Lose your chances

Eggs, foodstuffs, beer, all the other materials. There is another substance that played an important role in the genesis of photography, and this is ammonia. It's a chemical with many uses, but it's unpleasantly familiar to humans in the strong smell that can arise when urine is left to decay. And it's useful for making an image permanent, after the image has appeared on a surface, summoned by the action of sunlight. This fact was not always apparent.

Helmut and Alison Gernsheim, in *The History of Photography* (Oxford University Press, 1955), blame Humphrey Davy, the distinguished chemist who at the very start of the nineteenth century was investigating photography, for failing to notice the potential of ammonia. Davy had discovered how to make an image materialise on his paper, but he couldn't retain it; the pictures faded from sight. And though he was familiar with Carl Wilhelm Scheele's realization, from 1777, that "blackened silver chloride becomes insoluble in ammonia," Davy failed to draw the obvious conclusion from this fact: that he too could use ammonia to stabilize his images. By failing to apply his knowledge, he pissed away his chances of being a pioneer of fixing the photo.

What is this fixing? For Atkins' cyanotypes, it was enough simply to wash the visible image on the reactive page under water, after which the surface would not alter any more; water fixed the picture. For a calotype using the developing method, by contrast, the treated surface of the negative is exposed, then covered, but nothing seems to have happened, as I'm so agitated by, above. It's only later in time that the surface is further treated, at which point the magic does its work and the image starts to emerge. This is great, but you can't go too far, can't allow development to continue until the whole page is dark with picture. The photographer wants to halt at a certain point, when the right amount of light is differentiated on the negative, when there is still contrast. Water is not the right medium, in this process. Instead, by 1839 Herschel had discovered that a solution, known as "hypo," could be used as "fixer," to arrest the salts on the page at the appropriate moment and keep the image right. Not too dark with detail; not too pale. Only then do you bathe the negative in water to wash off any remaining chemicals and prevent further change. Herschel used sodium thiosulphate as his hypo; now the related ammonium thiosulphate is more commonly used, as it acts more quickly.

Basically, ammonia's a substance that helps to preserve the photographic image in the right proportions; at just the right moment, it fixes the chemicals in place.

## Clip off the amino groups

I have a previous interest in ammonia because of its important role in the nitrogen cycle, and thereby in the life of sharks. (See: *Sharks, Death, Surfers: An Illustrated Companion*, Sternberg Press, 2019.) The broad-brush picture is this: nitrogen circles through the air, and, converted into nitrates underground, it moves via being eaten from plants into living creatures; from their excretion or rotting bodies the nitrates re-enter the soil, from where some are turned back to nitrogen and released into the atmosphere. It's a chemical cycle. So it's essential for life, but different creatures process nitrogen in slightly different ways. Birds, for example, will excrete nitrogen, in the form of guano, onto statues, or onto bowler hats, or the Bush House construction site.

What's the process for sharks? Like other animals, they take in and use proteins, which contain nitrogen, but animal bodies do not use all this nitrogen and must dispose of much of it. The amino groups containing the nitrogen are turned into either ammonia, or the less toxic urea, and in most fish, these substances are liberally excreted. Sharks are not most fish. They convert their waste nitrogen into urea, but, instead of expelling it, sharks retain most of their urea, building it up into huge concentrations throughout the body. (This causes olfactory trouble if a dead shark is left to decay in the sun, and its urea reserves break down into ammonia.) This amount of urea would be fatal to most animals, but sharks have adapted not just to withstand, but to thrive on and require these high urea levels, which are useful for egg formation and for osmosis.

This sounds like abstruse elasmobranch biology, but it provides an analogue for photography. In the shark, the ammonia-related substance, urea, is stored in the body in concentration, locked in the cells, while only a little of the urea just washes out in the urine. That is, some chemicals stay held in their particular position, while others are washed away, preventing further reaction. It's like developing a negative: on the treated paper, the chemicals that have reacted are locked into their changed state by the ammoniac fixer. They stay there, in place, building up the areas of density, darkness, concentration. The soluble parts (which in this photography case are unexposed silver halides) are rinsed away from the surface, into the developing bath or down the drain. Some of the chemicals remain in place, while some are washed away, and it's the interplay between the retained salts and the ones that are disposed of that allows for the image (and the shark).

## We have boxes and boxes of them

Speaking of the shark as negative, there is another photographer whom it is illuminating to compare to Anna Atkins. It's the American Michael Light, born in 1963, who has several complementary modes of practice. One is going up in a small plane and taking aerial pictures of the vast landscapes. Another is an archival habit: he goes to large and powerful record-keeping organisations, rifles through their collections, and comes out with the images that interest him. He then reprints, reframes the images (in literal and figurative senses), moving them from the dusty cardboard boxes to the gallery walls, and to large photo books.

I think there is a parallel between this process—reprinting the item that was already there—and Atkins' cyanotype work from a century and a half earlier. There's a similar aspect of non-interference in the work of both Light and Atkins: I was out and about and I found this object that interested me, a seaweed or a negative from NASA, then I printed it. I put my object on top of the paper and let the sun do its work. And now I'm showing it to you.

One of the shark books in my own archive describes a mid-'60s invention designed to electrically shock sharks and divert them from people. The inventor hoped to sell the device to NASA, "for use by astronauts." It took me really a large number of readings of the book before the uneasy voice at the back of my mind surfaced with the explicit objection to this: but there are no sharks on the moon.

There are not, but there are plenty of oceanic images in Light's various projects. One such portfolio is concerned with the American moon exploration missions of the 1960s and '70s (published by Knopf in 1999 as *Full Moon*). I like that way that he shows space parachutes that look like jellyfish, and, the surface of the moon pocked with (could they be?) sea anemones. The stage separation of the Saturn 1b rocket, in 1968, in a daffodil-shaped blaze of fuel, looks just like Johnstone and Croall's nature print *Rhodophyllis bifida*, a seaweed from 1859. There's an Apollo 12 astronaut, captioned "Surrounded by Blue Aura Thought to be Water-Vapor Ice Crystals"—black sky, scurfy grey moon surface, and bisecting the horizon a little white figure in a haze of familiar blue. And the final photo in the series is a view after splashdown seen through a window hatch in 1973: there is a light sky, then the wide and elegant peaks and curves of the ocean waves in the sunlight, slightly frothing; they are a perfect, Atkins-cyanotype blue.

## Revisit the damage

Michael Light's other series in this mode of working with disinterred negatives (he's like Woolley, unpacking from the dust the proof of the glories of a former civilization), is with images from the U.S. National Archives and Los Alamos National Laboratory, of nuclear weapons testing in the 1950s and early '60s. This work was exhibited and published (by Knopf) in 2003 as *100 Suns*. Here, Light looks at explosions both domestic, in the Nevada desert, and abroad, in the Pacific. They're terrifying. For each image that he uses, he lists the name of the particular test and the larger operation it belonged to, its explosive power in kilotons or (the thousand-times greater) megatons, the location, precise time, original photographer, and more. He explains what the detonation was intended to research, and points out details in the image.

There's something destabilising, stereoscopic, about realizing that Light presents pictures of the actual explosions that caused the damage that Emmet Gowin went back to photograph, from his plane, forty-five years later. (Gowin mentions in his essay within *The Nevada Test Site* that the authorities there offered him their archive of negatives to look at and reprint, but he declined, wanting to make his own.) Light's *Image 42, Easy* is an orange-filtered aerial image (which makes it look instantly apocalyptic, or even more so) of "a prototype of the Mark 7 bomb," "showing a clearly visible shockwave effect on the alluvial desert soil." Easy (each bomb was named; this one was part of Operation Buster) was detonated at 8:30 am on 5th November 1951, at 1,314 feet, with a yield of thirty-one kilotons. The photo is of a huge mushroom cloud rising above the desert floor, dwarfing the mountains behind. It looks like an alien spraying destructor beams of pure light out of its eyes (which is not so far from the truth).

Gowin's *Plate 6, Yucca Flat*, from 1996, is a monochrome picture of the same space; you can recognize the shape of the mountain peaks behind the flat, but of course the cloud and the brightness are no longer there. (Gowin too gives dates, names, descriptions, and he adds the precision of geolocational co-ordinates, for every image.) Gowin's caption, too, specifies that this area is where Easy was tested (there was occasional reduplication of names within the programs—but we're getting used to repeated names). But Gowin explains in his notes that the above-ground explosions mostly left little evidence. There wasn't anything up there, at a thousand feet, for them to destroy or to make a mark on; the point, the test, was more about observing the fallout, the extent of the effects, how the radioactive material would distribute itself over the surrounding area (and beyond, as far as the Southern cotton fields). It's from the subterranean tests, dropped down deep shafts, that the visible traces remain, the subsidence craters. In his photos you can see, all over the desert, Nazca-like circles on the ground caused by these underground explosions, which obliterated a vast mass of material below the surface. Matter simply went, and no longer supported some of the substance above.

What are the appropriate words of destruction? It depends on the scale of what you're destroying. To make cardboard or paper you just take a tree and pulp it, cutting and crushing it small and mixing this with water. Pulverized is different—that means, turned to dust. Like a book whose pages crumble when you finally take it off the shelf, open the covers. Like bodies and their grave goods in tombs that have been preserved in the sealed, dark space for thousands of years, only for the archaeologist to let in new air, and the reed mat crumbles away.

And pulverized is not vaporized, which has a technical meaning (of the boiling or evaporation of a liquid to a gas), but which we use colloquially to describe being vanished, destroyed to existlessness. The dusty Nevada desert was not just vaporized when the bombs were tested there: some of the sand over the surface was instead melted into glass (the particular form known as trinitite) by the intense heat. Or tracing the same idea further back, there are parts of bodies found at Vesuvius (Leonard Woolley didn't know this, but he might like it) to which the same thing happened: P. Petrone, in the reasonably self-explanatory "Heat-Induced Brain Vitrification from the Vesuvius Eruption in C.E. 79" (*New England Journal of Medicine*, 2020), reports the discovery of "vitrified human brain tissues"—the extreme heat of the volcanic ash cloud had turned a man's brain into fragments of glass or glaze, little twisted shards that look like shrapnel.

In Light's re-versions of photos of the nuclear testing there are also some that resemble jellyfish, with the domed heads of the explosion and trailing legs, and the tethering ropes and projectile trails looking just like the tendrils of a mermaid's purse, like seaweed fronds. I like the way that Light thinks he is showing space, or nuclear explosion, but I keep seeing sea-creatures and seaweed. What I like about Atkins' work is the converse. She shows sea-things that look like clouds. Like dendrites in the brain, or like drowned hair waving. Drifty white clouds, in little shapes and trails, like something falling, gently, through the sky. Some of her structures, like a seaweed, branching, converging, follow the logic of the branches of a tree.

## Make mine a double

After the aerial and the archive, Michael Light has a third mode of photography, which follows on from his nuclear interest: the submarine. In addition to the Nevada desert tests, the U.S. carried out a series of post-war nuclear tests around the Marshall Islands, in the North Pacific (it's not so far, by coincidence, from where the *Pequod* sinks in *Moby-Dick*). These included underwater detonations, ground surface ones, and the strange Operation Crossroads, investigating the effects of nuclear weapons on ships at sea. A fleet of decommissioned (or, ghost) ships were hauled to Bikini Atoll lagoon, and bombed; around nine vessels remain on the seafloor there, offloaded to care of the Marshall Islands and popular with divers.

Pigment print, *"The Rinconada Oak" Seen as a Point Cloud, Heritage Tree #2, 75' Tall, 120' Wide and 200 Years Old, Palo Alto, California*, Michael Light, USA, 2017.

The artist fed some 850 drone images into visualization software to generate about eighty million points representing the exterior and "extrapolated interior" of the tree. All this rapid-fire technology, as Light points out in a 2017 interview with the organisation Canopy, to depict what are "far and away the oldest and most patient living things in the region."

There was later testing in the area in the early 1950s, including the Castle Bravo detonation, at fifteen megatons the U.S.'s largest explosion. (The Hiroshima explosion, for comparison, was fifteen kilotons: a thousand times smaller.) So after his *100 Suns* project, Light went in person to Bikini Atoll, taking photos above-ground, and diving down into the Bravo crater, among the ruined ships, to make videos, filming in the utter cold and dark. In a 2013 interview on the architecture website *BLDGBLG*, Light explains the dangers:

> You take on a tremendous amount of nitrogen down there. It's pretty technical. You have to do decompression diving, which is inherently dangerous—you have to breathe helium trimix at about thirty feet below the boat for nearly an hour after twenty minutes at depth, hoping that no tiger shark comes along to eat you, as you adjust. [. . .]It's very entropic. You're suffering, at that depth, from nitrogen narcosis. It's like having three martinis. You're pretty zonked out.

And in Light's photos and videos, when he thought he was filming the ships, down into the cold depth, what was it kept sidling into the viewfinder, scaring him? It was sharks, of course. They glide past. There's a decision Light made about his stills and films in this *Black Bravo* project, which is to present them as negative images, light and dark reversed. So when he stares upwards from the ocean floor, he stares at a fierce black sun, and little white bubbles rise up from his breathing device. When a shark comes past its body casts a pale shadow on the sand. He does this, I think, as a way of conveying the strangeness: some of the images are underwater, for a start, which is the wrong place, for the art-making human, for any person. Then, the tone reversal highlights the comparison from his work *100 Suns*, that each nuclear device, with its vast energy, is an analogue of the sun itself. There should be one only, illuminating the scene, providing us with all the light we will ever have, except in this case, the vast light of the explosions has fundamentally altered the scene, reversed the lighting. It's a site, a proof of something utterly wrong, that people have done: made the bomb, sunk the ships, caused so much damage. Of course it's negative, negatives.

There's a similarity between Light's underwater photos and the photogram of the shark egg case. (Which was kept in an album associated with the photo-enthusiatic Bright family. From Bright to Light—names and themes keep recurring.) The case has been taken from the sea (washed up on shore, gathered), so it too is in the wrong zone now. And the version of the image that we have is also a negative; the plasticky green egg case was placed against the white salted paper, and out came a pale, almost pink shape floating on the dark brown background. We don't know what happened to the eggs that were inside, whether the case worked as a protective shell for the potential sharks within. But being preserved in the surface of the photograph is another sort of floating on down through the ages. As the earliest commentators alluded to or intuited, a photograph is a form of birth, regeneration, a continuity. And if everything is mobile and floating like this, at what point do we capture and preserve it? What's the best time, what's the right way to see, when we're flipping between positive and negative, toggling between the underwater, the liquid and the solid, the print, the retelling, the memory?

# Refixing the Image

*photo*

Anything to do with light, so, plants that are *phototropic* turn towards the sun, as opposed to *scototropic* plants, whose roots burrow towards the dark, down into the rubble.

Things related to the practice of photography, taking pictures. All sorts of compounds associated with this, such as *photoclinometry*–deriving topographical information from measurements of the relative brightness shown in aerial photographs.

*Photo* precedes the names of chemical salts and processes, to express the fact that light changes their molecular constitution, which is of use in the habit of photography.

# The mirror of the sea

In the last chapter I've been discussing examples from the early days of photography, of how organic materials were used as components in the emerging processes. Pulling the focus up to today, I'll consider two recent obituaries that show how animals can be used not just as raw material, but as inspiration for innovations in optics. I also want to discuss how photography allows for repetition in perhaps unexpected ways, for having an image twice.

Obituarist Daniel Osorio describes Michael Land, neuroscientist, (born 12th April 1942, died 14th December 2020) as "the Marco Polo of the visual sciences. He visited exotic parts of the animal kingdom, and showed that almost every way humans have discovered to bend, reflect, shape and image light with mirrors and lenses is also used by some creature's eye" (the *Guardian*, 19th January 2021). Land noticed, for instance, that scallops' eyes focus light not with a lens as humans' do, but using "a concave mirror in the manner of a Newtonian telescope," while butterflies have, under each facet lens of the eye, a complete Galilean telescope for collimating (making parallel) the incoming light. Which of us would not be proud to have an obituary containing the encomium that "His 1976 discovery that prawns focus light not by lenses, but with a structure of mirror-lined boxes, helped lead to the discovery of a method to focus X-rays"?

We have also, Horace Barlow, neuroscientist, born 8th December 1921, died 5th July 2020. While Land is interested in the actions and the use of the eye, Barlow takes a perhaps more underlying approach, going down a stratum of perception. From a starting point of investigating how frogs look out for flies to unroll their tongues onto, "he developed theories to account for the relationship between what neurons are doing and the corresponding visual experience." His work encompassed computer and information science, signal redundancy, statistical probability. Georgina Ferry in a *Guardian* obituary (of 23$^{rd}$ August 2020) explains:

> "Instead of thinking of neural representations as transformations of stimulus energies," wrote Barlow in a typically elegant summary after decades of work, "we should regard them as approximate estimates of the probable truths of hypotheses about the current environment."

Barlow is explaining here how the brain fills in gaps in the information that is delivered to it, how we (and frogs) process visual material to build a fuller understanding of the world around us. A little data is enough to prompt a huge construction of supposition. I love this, in Barlow's scientific rigour about vision, that he steps back from certainty to something less precise: to estimates of probables of hypotheses. These levels of doubt remind me of the archaeological mode of proceeding: the things that we see let us remake and understand, but only to a certain extent. The model we rebuild will be the best we can make, but it will always be an interpretation, rather than a mechanical, exact duplicate.

This is also how mobile phones and other digital cameras process information in order to take photos. They don't neutrally record what they are pointed at, but (to a greater extent than the analogue camera does) they receive data, process and adapt it according to the instructions they've been given, and they make assumptions about what should be included within any image, given previous experience of what might be there. (This is a concern for Pierre Huyghe, whose exhibition *UUmwelt* at the Serpentine Gallery, 2018, looked at describing and re-forming images, with the help of animals.)

There's another strand that interests me, about when the living creature does not provide ingredients or material, nor yet inspiration, but is itself, as an intact whole, part of the system. Particularly: an experiment carried out by shark scientists Karl Kuchnow and Perry Gilbert, and described in a paper in Gilbert, Mathewson and Rall's 1967 book, *Sharks, Skates and Rays*, which consists of papers from a symposium held in the Bahamas the previous year. There's a whole section in this book on "Central Nervous System and Special Senses," which includes vision, and this paper by Kuchnow (and Gilbert, but I'll draw a curtain over him, for ease of discussion) is on "Pupillary and Tapetal Pigment Responses in the Lemon Shark, *Negaprion Brevirostris*."

## Rendered silver by crystals

Kuchnow, conjuror-like, is investigating light and mirrors. His sphere of reference is the tapetum lucidum (*tapetum*—a heavy cloth with inwrought figures, a carpet, tapestry; *lucidum*—bright, shining; both from the Latin), which is a layer of platelets on the inside back of the shark's eyeball, behind the retina. In one state, these platelets are "rendered silver by crystals of guanine," as the scientist poetically puts it, and this makes them reflective. There are thousands of the platelets, and they lie not on a radius of the spherical eyeball but angled all round the back, so that each one faces as directly as possible towards the pupil and the incoming light. Like a tiny version of the array of panels spread out over a huge field, in a solar farm.

Each platelet is made of a chemical compound called guanine. This substance was first isolated and named in the mid-nineteenth century, when the chemist Julius Unger extracted it from guano, which is, how shall I put it, the droppings of birds or bats (bird guano is probably better-known, on account of being more prolifically produced, adjacent to more people). Albrecht Kossel followed this with Nobel-winning work on guanine as one of the compounds present in nucleic acid, a discovery that paved the way for later understanding of DNA, while V. Franz in 1905 noticed that guanine was present in the eyeball of the shark. Guano, this original source for guanine, has a distinguished history. It's been used in many agricultural societies as a fertilizer, on account of containing nitrogen and other helpful substances. As well as promoting crop growth, guano can be used in the manufacture of saltpetre, needed for gunpowder; it was in demand during the U.S. Civil War, when saltpetre was otherwise unavailable to the South. Guano helps plants to grow, and it helps people to blow each other up. Nineteenth-century Europeans coming to South America and the Pacific appreciated that it could be a rich resource if exported; international demand and a profitable industry boomed. (Joseph Conrad's *Nostromo* of 1904, set in Costaguana and with silver at the heart of the plot, points to a violent interplay between wealth, exploitation, and worthless crap.)

The silvery guanine in the shark's eye plays exactly the same role as the layer of silver behind glass in a human mirror; that is, it bounces the rays back out. When light comes into the eyeball it is registered once as it passes through the retina. The tapetum behind then reflects the light back, and the retina can use it again. This process improves the creature's ability to use the limited light at its disposal; it's a way to see better. (It also has the side effect of making the shark's eyes gleam in the dark; extra-aquatically, cats have the same mechanism.) The shark uses the light twice, having first one vision of a scene, then a minuscule amount of time later, another. And this is a vital comparison: photography, too, allows you to see something twice, once when it happens, then again after a delay when you consider the photograph. Mirrors, as well, show you a second you. And time: every memory, every image of the self in the past, is not the present thinker, but an old double. That's what the lemon shark's guanine in the eyeball stirs up: repetition, reflection, duplication through time.

## I want to paint it black

But back to the back of the eye. The situation becomes more complex when we learn that the tapetum lucidum does not stay in one state. In a brighter environment, the shark does not need this double-dose of daylight, and it temporarily decommissions the shiny tapetum. How? Alongside each tapetum platelet is another region, empty in the first instance, but which can be filled with a pigment made of melanin granules. When more light from outside is entering the shark's eyeball, these melanin granules roll through from their storage reservoir until every surface of and around the platelets is surrounded by pigment. The tapetum is occluded, and ceases to perform its reflective function. In this state, light enters the retina only once and is sent on through the optic nerve up to the brain. Any excess is absorbed by the darker melanin rather than reflected back for a repeated use. It's like inking over a mirror: black pigment means that the silvery surface no longer reflects the light, which can't be used a second time. Or like redacting a document.

This is the situation in the lemon shark's eye, and this is the biological arena in which Kuchnow is digging for more detail. He wants to know: how does the shark's eye move between these two states, of guanine-shiny tapetum, and melanin-occluded tapetum; between reusing the reflected light, and darkly absorbing it? What's prompting the influx of the melanin: does the brain respond to stimulus and give instruction to flood the spaces, or is it a strictly autonomic reaction, done as a reflex by these specialist parts of the eyeball with no input from the brain? I am prompted to extend the scope of the question: is it a mechanical process, or is there calculation and instruction involved? Is it like old-fashioned, chemical photography, or like digital, algorithmic image processing? Is it cause, or reason?

The second strand of Kuchnow's investigation is into time: how long does the actual inflow of melanin take, how long before it clears away, after becoming superfluous. Then, how long does the shark's brain need, to get used to and process this altered dose of brightness? What time lag is there as the light changes in the environment, in the eyeball, in the brain's perception? What delays might there be, and what is the shark waiting for, to get its image?

And again, to follow the implication of Kuchnow's questions, to extend our reach beyond his line of inquiry: I'm interested in the same questions, but as applied not to lemon sharks but to Victorian photographic pioneers. What were their processes of inducing chemical change on the surface, and how long did they have to wait; what was the significance of delay, pause, of the intrusion of time into what they wanted to obtain?

I'm interested, really, in the same questions for all of us: what is the importance of time, pooling through into our perceptual processes, until we get what it is that we wanted to know? What image was being made, what was it that someone was trying to show us all along, how much time does it take to understand?

## Hook me up to the circuit

To consider these questions, Kuchnow creates a system in which the living creature is part of a light-examining circuit. Like the photographer is part of the photo-taking set-up. Like we are part of larger systems, an essential part.

A lemon shark, less than two feet long, is placed in a tank, next to a ruler and a grey scale, for reference. The experiment takes place in daytime, but starts with a black blanket covering the tank to make it dark. Outside the tank is a camera with a synchronized flash. "The method, quite simple," explains Kuchnow, is to flash a light at the shark's eye and take a picture of it at the same time. If, in this dark environment, the shark's eye has all its guanine exposed, it will reflect back more of the light, and the film in the camera will record this. Conversely, if the cover is taken off, the shark's eye will adjust to daylight, and the eye's platelets will cloud with melanin. This means that they will absorb more light, less will be available to reflect back to land on the camera film, and the chemicals there will be less affected. So this is what Kuchnow does: adjust the curtain round the tank, and thereby the light levels, to see how this guanine/melanin balance changes, and how long it takes to do so. That's his process, fiddling with the light and the timing.

And when he's tried in the various scenarios, a range of light to dark, Kuchnow then develops this regular 35mm camera film and measures the density of the chemicals remaining on its surface. Where lots of light has reached the silver halide of the film's surface, the crystals react by converting to metallic silver. When this is fixed in place (as per Herschel's discovery, above), the exposed crystals appear on the negative as blackness, to varying degrees of solidity. Of course if they were then printed as a positive image, a photo from the negative, these exposed areas would reverse, becoming light again; they're depicting the points on the shark's retina of maximum guanine-crystal brightness. (The scientific paper doesn't provide, though I would like to see, photos printed from this film, back from the chemist's, to be rifled through like holiday snaps.)

Parts of the film that were not touched by light do not convert to metallic silver. They remain as silver halide and are washed away during the developing process, leaving transparent the parts of the film base that did carry them. These particles of silver end up in the developing fluid, from which they can be extracted, like when a forty-niner pans for gold in the rivers of California.

So Kuchnow ends up with a set of photographic negatives and, by measuring the thickness of the dark metallic silver on each negative, he can apply various calculations and end up correlating the density of silver on the film to the amount of guanine exposed in the shark's eye under various conditions. And he charts the curve of how fast the eyeball adjusts when the light is changed, how quickly the melanin can flood in or return to its reservoir, and how long the brain takes to catch up with the information it's receiving from and about these chemical processes.

That's his investigation: what the photographic silver lets him measure about the silvery mirror in the eye, and how time affects this. I think this is a very beautiful experiment, looking at photos, silver, inkiness, darkness, and time. And sharks.

## Where am I looking?

Kuchnow's experiment uses the guanine-silvered mirror of the shark's eye to reflect the light back to the camera. He uses standard, consumer Kodak film, but if I were assigning a line of photographic descent I reckon I'd take the French route and would trace Kuchnow's shark (with its angled, shining platelets) back to Daguerre, with his images on the tilted silvered plate, rather than to Talbot, who made his pictures on fibrous paper. Although the rougher surface of Talbot's calotype is more like the textured, toothed skin of a shark. Paper-like, made of mirrors, retentive of chemicals: the shark is photographic inside and out.

Kuchnow's shark work prompts me to reflect on a set of photos in MoMA's collection of early photography, as discussed by historian Geoffrey Batchen (in his essay in *Photography at MoMA 1840-1920*, 2017). This is, a group of photos about items that were on show at another museum: the South Kensington Museum, which grew into today's V&A. In 1853 the Museum borrowed a range of elaborate, wood- or silver-framed mirrors dating from the fifteenth century, and asked the photographer Charles Thurston Thompson to make a record of these items. He did this, setting up his stand and camera for a front-on image of each piece. It was easy to show the frames, with their curlicues of crowns, fish, flowers (they're reminiscent of Ortelius' blue-ink template pages, in his memory book).

But how could Thompson take a picture of the mirror's glass without inadvertently including the equipment too, without the photographer crowding into the shot and spoiling it? He solved this problem, explains Batchen, "by simply ignoring it": in the photo's surface, which is also the mirror's glass, we also see whatever else was around. Here's a gardener, tending the flower-beds. There is Thompson looking at his watch, timing the exposures, and there is the black, curtained box of the camera, pointing its lens straight at the mirror, the photographer, the one who looks. But we are not pictured in this mirror; we seem to have swum off-screen.

MoMA has prints of Thompson's images now, as does the V&A. But the mirrors themselves aren't in the collections; they were only photographed because they were on loan, before being returned to the owners. The image remains though the object has long gone.

Mirrors have been within cameras for a long time. The Gernsheims in *The History of Photography* gaze back centuries, describing convex and flat mirrors in the early camera obscuras. They note that the monk and scientist Johann Zahn, who worked around 1685, had looped ahead of his time: "Zahn's cameras are prototypes of nineteenth-century box and reflex cameras," the only thing lacking being the invention of chemical photography itself. When the chemical processes for fixing the image did present themselves, the mirror was already in place in the camera, with Daguerre and others incorporating them into the camera set-up, so that the photographer might see the image right way up, then capture it.

I'd trace rather further back when considering the mirror and vision, back to Perseus in Greek mythology trying to cut off the head of the Gorgon, Medusa. If Perseus had looked at her directly, he risked being turned to stone, but by looking into the reflection in the polished metal of Athena's shield, he was able to approach and strike at her. (I pick up an echo of Medusa in Spielberg's invention of the moment, in *Jaws* the film, when the detached head of Ben

Gardner looms into the frame.) The mirror gives rise to considera-
tion of the idea of looking at something, but not directly.

## A picture of the shadow of the flame

What things can only be photographed in an indirect manner? The
question opens a can of worms, or a coiffure of snakes. It might be
a technical constraint, that our normal method of pointing a camera at an object won't work, physically, in certain circumstances.
Although there's usually a way round, eventually.

Take schlieren photography and the shadowgraph, related
techniques that allow the depiction of refraction—the phenomenon of how light changes direction as it enters a region (in air or
water) of new density. (Diffraction, in contrast, is the bending of a
wave round a corner or through a gap.) Such a change in density
can be caused by a change in heat, or by the application of pressure, or through mixing two substances, but it's not usually visible
to the naked eye; we can't see it. It can, however, be photographed,
using the right set-up.

A light source, a collimating mirror, an object, a camera:
these are needed for the simpler shadowgraph system, while
adding a knife edge to block some rays allows for the more complex schlieren imaging (the name is from the German *schlieren*,
to smear). The scientist Harold Edgerton, working at MIT from
the 1920s through to the '80s, produced probably the best-known
shadowgraphs: the shockwaves that follow the path of a bullet
through air; the heat whorls and spirals above a candle flame, the
swirling patterns as hot water and cold mix up, become indistinct. (Edgerton was constantly curious: in addition to schlieren
techniques, he was a pioneer of strobe lighting, which allowed
for ultra-fast photography, separating flowing time into discrete
frames of incredibly short moments. Marey-esque physical movement, the splash from a drop of milk, the processes at the moment

of detonating a nuclear bomb, Stonehenge lit up at night to make aerial photos—all these were his.)

These two methods, schlieren photography and shadow-graphs, show not the air, but the effect on light of the air; they are indirect ways of making an image. Sometimes it's not the technology but the photographer, rather, who is unable to look face on at the subject, or who chooses not to. They present the event at one remove, depicting what it causes, not what it is. I'm thinking about D. A. Pennebaker's film *Faces of November* (1964), which shows the assassination of JFK, but not straight on; shows it by way of filming the faces of Americans watching the president's coffin train go past. Reactions, aftermath, ruins.

This question, of when is an image directly caused by something, when is it at a remove, reminds me of my concern over Brody's typewriter task in *Jaws*, when he has to distinguish between the cause and the reason—quarrel, illness, revenge. What's the cause of this normal photo? Light has bounced off objects consistently according to their colour absorbency and landed on the receptive paper. And this schlieren photo? Refracted light has travelled through regions of different qualities and arrived in differing quantities. It's one step less straightforward, at a degree removed. It's like comparing the Zapruder footage from 1963 with Pennebaker's film. What does this first film show? A bullet hitting the president as he is driven through Dallas. And this one? The effect of the bullet, the other shockwaves.

## A Spanish gentleman, sir?

While we're thinking about photography at one step removed, there is an interesting question of how you might represent a photograph in any medium that is not itself the photo. Historian Larry Schaaf has a post ("Revelations & Representations," 27th May 2016, on the *Talbot Catalogue Raisonné Blog* hosted by the Bodleian, Oxford) about the problem that nineteenth-century magazines and newspapers had with describing and representing this exciting new medium. How could they explain what it was, when they did not yet have the technology to reproduce the photo onto their own pages; how can you show an image of a photo if you don't have the means to just print a photo?

It's a problem that clearly exercised Hergé, when in *The Red Sea Sharks* (first published in colour, book format in French in 1958; in English, 1960) he has his drawn cartoon character Tintin look through the photographs in his friend Alcazar's wallet. We know they are photos because they are drawn with extra simplicity of style, by using a few tones of grey, with a white border round each image. On the same page Hergé has Tintin draw a picture of Alcazar, hoping the hotel clerk will recognize it, and the action raises an ontological ouroboros: if a cartoon character draws a mug-shot of a friend, is there not a danger that the drawing becomes real? After all, Tintin, wielding the pencil, is also "just" a drawn face on the page. But the skilled Hergé can easily manipulate the levels of reality, the status of the image. He has control of the sketch, the photo, the real, within his world of representation.

## Old hat, new hat

So there are matters to consider about what falls within the purview of photography, and about what can be represented, in what media. There is also a simpler question, of, what can you take a photograph of and what can't you? Or, it seems like a simple question.

You might answer with a whole list of criteria; you can't take a photo of something that's: too big, too small, too near, too far, too fast, too slow. But wait! Let's consider some of the hindrances, as they don't always fit, or, they seem to change into subtly different objections.

Something too far away—that might be, space and the far parts of the universe. But there are ways to overcome this, as Peter Galison's work on black holes nods to.

Too big—this would seem to be the same as too close, in that I can't take a picture that would make a meaningful image of the whole of this object, because I am right up by it. That is, the item would fill the photo, and there would be no context or companion to compare it to, to give a sense of what it is in relation to anything else. It would become, instead, too isolated. Can an object be too lonely to be photographed?

Too small? When my first daughter was born in 2008, she was not a huge baby. Everybody in South Africa, where we lived then, would greet her in friendly fashion, and tell me that when she sleeps, she grows. She didn't sleep too well, but she did grow, at her own pace, and I began to get annoyed with the other frequent comment, of, isn't she small! No. And, it depends how close you're standing, anyway. In her baby carrier, snuggling right up by me, she didn't seem small; she was just right.

Something that's actually too small, or lasts for too short a stretch of time, happens too fast? This is the problem that Harold Edgerton was addressing, with his incorporation of strobe lighting into ultra-fast photography. Something that happens at a scale of time of longer duration than we can capture, or easily imagine? I'd propose here the fossil as a form of image construction: there's an organic material reacting to a lack of light in an enclosed compartment, in the mud, and the chemical makeup changes until it is a new substance, one that carries the grainy, monochrome image down through millennia.

Something that's not there. Something not on the visible light spectrum (though inventors like Talbot were onto this concept from the very start of their investigations), or made of the wrong material. Something that's invisible, by virtue of being abstract (or just invisible). Sunken too deep underwater. Too dangerous. Too personal, too private. Too radioactive; too obscured. With something standing in front of it, blocking the trajectory of the light. Something that's in the future, or from too far ago in the past? Something too vampiric, or otherwise resistant or with an aversion to appearing in the mirror, the screen, the photo. I like the claim made in *Dora Lives: The Authorized Story of Miki Dora* (by C. R. Stecyk III and Drew Kampion, T.Adler Books, 2005) about the surf rebel extraordinaire Dora: that he had the ability to not show up in photos. He was there at the taking, standing next to the other people who appear in the finished print, but "He disappeared from the film!" (exclaims the witness), sliding off the emulsion, out the frame. (In this, the surfer is unlike the eminent archaeologist Leonard Woolley, who does get caught on the film, pinned and preserved, repeated.)

## It's not boring here

There's one specific argument about what cannot be photographed that caught my attention when I was reading the obituary of bacteriologist and epidemiologist Ephraim "Andy" Anderson (born 28th October 1911, died 14th March 2006), who pioneered the microphotography needed to take pictures of phages bursting out of bacteria.

I note that Anderson was director of the Enteric Reference Laboratory based at Colindale, London, which is also the place where the British Library used to house its newspaper and magazine archive (until 2013). There's clearly something in the water, in this undistinguished suburb, that makes it good for gathering and comparing information. We know what a reference library is; a reference laboratory is a central facility for carrying out additional analysis on samples from primary labs such as those in hospitals. It's different from a surveillance lab, which collects data in order to plan and monitor public health. And "enteric" is everything to do with the intestine.

The argument writhing round Anderson is, can you take a picture of something that is too small in itself, or too small for our equipment? Anderson's specialities were typhoid and antibiotic resistance, but he also made important contributions in the field of seeing and photographing bacteriophages. His very interesting *Guardian* obituary (22nd March 2006, by Anthony Tucker) explains:

> This he did by using ultra-violet fluorescence to visualize the tiny dots of genetic material in bacteriophages (bacterial viruses), whose diameter is barely 1/20th of a micron and which, according to routine resolution theory, are far too small to be seen. This achievement, creating a low-cost laboratory technique employing ordinary optics for the investigation of viruses, was revealed in an elegant paper, Observation of Virus Growth with Aminoacrinides, at London University during the ninth symposium of the Society of General Microbiology in 1959.

> This important work by Anderson and his group was promptly denounced as "impossible" by their peers—predominantly by the Nobel laureate Salvador Luria, an influential expert on phages, who had delivered the keynote paper and dominated debate at the meeting. Electron microscopy had, by this time, revealed the true and miniscule dimensions of the phages, which hitherto had been regarded as unfilterable and invisible. Luria confused the wavelength-based limits of resolution of light micro-scopy with the limits of visibility; his declaration that Anderson's micrographs were spurious was technically wrong and unjustified. It was, however, widely accepted and damaging.

## We all make mistakes

It's reassuring that even a Nobel laureate can confuse the wavelength-based limits of resolution with the limits of visibility. These terms might require a bit of illumination. The wavelength is the distance between the peak of one wave and the peak of the next.

(It's not the amplitude, which is the distance between the undisturbed position and the peak of the wave.) It's the wavelength of the light source that limits the highest resolution that an optical system can distinguish.

The human eye, for example, can usually detect that two grains of sand sitting one tenth of a millimeter apart are not the same; any closer together than that and we'd read them as just one, slightly-less-tiny dot. You can see the grains better using a magnifying glass or telescope, but it doesn't work to just use stronger and stronger lenses. No matter how good your eyes, the highest resolution discernible is half the size of the wavelength of the light source. Which means that using a light microscope, with light in the visible wavelength range of 380 to 700 nanometers, the smallest object that can be distinguished would measure about two hundred nanometers, or about the size of a bacterium. Anything smaller and you'd need to use an electron microscope, which, with its much smaller wavelength, can distinguish smaller items.

Basically, Anderson used ultraviolet to make the phages show up, but Luria thought that because a microscope couldn't normally separate them, they must be invisible. Anderson was vindicated and praised, but only after a long delay. The confusion arose at the crossroads between the size of the object, and the properties of the viewing and recording technology.

It's a problem that persists, discussed by forensic investigator and architect Eyal Weizman, in *Forensic Architecture: Violence at the Threshold of Detectability* (Zone Books, 2017). This threshold is where he investigates "things that hover between being identifiable and not," starting with images made by U.S. reconnaissance planes over an extermination camp in 1944. At issue is the fact that each grain of silver halide on a film was able to record information about a space on the ground that measured half a meter square, which is roughly the area a human inhabits, and the same size as the roof shafts on a crematorium. It's the physical state of our recording material, as well as of our surroundings, that constrains our images, and provides ample material for dispute.

These arguments, about what a photo does show and what it can show, rely on the physical properties of light; there are rules underpinning our images. The equations of resolution, pertinent here, were first described in a formula devised by Ernst Karl Abbe in 1873. Before that the Astronomer Royal, George Biddell Airy, had set out the idea that there is a smallest point of light that can be focused through a microscope; this is the Airy disk, which will "not be a point but a bright circle surrounded by a series of bright rings." Airy ends his discussion paper ("On the Diffraction of an Object-glass with Circular Aperture," *Transactions of the Cambridge Philosophical Society*, 1837) with a lovely phrase, though he's only mentioning the idea to dismiss it, "viz. that if waves spread equally in all directions, there could be no such thing as darkness." There could be. We know that there is.

## Purple the sails . . . the oars were silver

Considering all these possible restrictions on what one might photograph, it's starting to sound like a *moderata durant* kind of activity, to return to the phrase that Georg Braun used in his inscription in Ortelius' autograph album—things in moderation last. Photography, like ruling over conquered Troy, is the sort of activity that requires a middle route. Not too big, not too small. Proceed not too tightly, not too loosely. If you go to an extreme, you'll end up losing your arms in the shallow waters, you'll disappoint Patrolman Len Hendricks just as he's trying to pull you to safety. You'll be left blurry, as Antony says in a beautiful line in Shakespeare's *Antony & Cleopatra* (IV.xiv. lines 9–14):

> That which is now a horse, even with a thought

> The rack dislimns and makes it indistinct
> As water is in water.
> [. . .] now thy captain is
> Even such a body: here I am Antony,
> Yet cannot hold this visible shape, my knave.

He's losing his identity, like an area of atmospheric pressure in the shipping forecast. Falling more slowly. But his immediately preceding words are interesting, too:

> Sometimes we see a cloud that's dragonish,
> A vapour sometime like a bear or lion,
> A tower'd citadel, a pendent rock,
> A forked mountain, or blue promontory
> With trees upon't, that nod unto the world,
> And mock our eyes with air: thou hast seen these signs;
> They are black vesper's pageants.

Antony, in the midst of defeat, betrayal, and carnage at sea, takes a moment to wax lyrical to his servant, saying that clouds, the airy disks, are deceptive. He's talking specifically about the impermanence of images: we think we see these items, up on the sky, drawn in white on the blue, but the next moment they are gone. Pictures, "this visible shape" of an entity, don't hold.

Antony's "The rack dislimns" is, fittingly, an indistinct and convoluted phrase. In a violent age, it could refer, homophonically or misspelled, to a body's limbs being ripped apart on a torture instrument. Or to a rack where a painting is drying or a canvas is stretched, but in this case the lines of the painting are losing their shape (a limner is a painter). But the more you look, the more meanings there are, around 1600, to "rack" and "wrack," related as they both are to "wreck," with its implications of ruin, destruction, a shattered person. Equinely speaking, "rack" is a sort of sideways gallop, an ungainly gait that might threaten to unbalance and undo the horse. Or could Antony be alluding to "wrack," an ocean term, to describe the froth of the sea, the white patterns of the wave-tops, as they lose their outlines and return to the un-individuated whole? I too am going to return to indistinctness, he says: there are these pictures against the blue background, then they go. Then everything's gone. It's as though, during a hiatus in the chaos, he's looking right forwards through time at some of Anna Atkins' seaweed images—and "wrack" is a type of seaweed, too, found on the tidal line—but then he can't see them any more. He hasn't yet seen his empire come crashing down in dust, but I think he thinks it's coming, something's coming, out of the sky and cloud shapes. And by the time Atkins' cyanotypes really do come along? Antony will be dead by then, will be such a body.

## Spirits in the machine

One penultimate aspect of what can't you photograph: you can't make photos of the dead, of spirits, of things not of this world. This would be on account of the fact that there are no ghosts, so they can't be photographed. A different suggestion, though, would be that this is a "wrong area of the electromagnetic spectrum" question, as though with the right equipment—not an infrared camera but an infra-dead—we might get the image of non-material aspects of the person. And we do! Exactly from the era of Arthur Conan Doyle and the spiritualist explosion of the First World War, platoons of pictures of spirits, ghosts, of the aura. What is that? It's your spirit, or non-corporeal aspect, or a plasma field of energy glowing round you. It's most of the name of "Laura."

Then perhaps more definitive, is a final objection: I cannot take a picture, make a photo of this, because photography is just not the right medium to convey what it is I want to show you.

This leads right into the opening of *Twin Peaks*, which is—it's hard to pin-point: an epic artwork, a pageant of forked mountains, a long-term tele-cinematic project devised by American auteurs David Lynch and Mark Frost. It incorporates three series of roughly

Ink on paper, inscription by Georg Braun on page 100r of the *Album Amicorum* of Abraham Ortelius, put together in the Low Countries between c. 1574 and 1596.

hour-long, individual episodes, the first two of which were broadcast on television in 1990 and 1991 (and re-run in 1992, with an excellent introduction to each episode delivered by the Log Lady). Also in the stable are one stand-alone film, and a handful of books. After a long delay, the third series, *Twin Peaks: The Return*, appeared in 2017, by which time most viewers were watching its eighteen episodes on their computers or other internet-connected devices.

*Twin Peaks* requires a lot of attention, and, as evident from its duration, a big investment of time. Which is fitting, as time, its malleability, disturbance, illusory nature, is one of the concerns of the artwork. (There's a lot of material contained within *Twin Peaks*; you can make a case for almost anything being one of it concerns. But I'm dwelling on time.) Time and photography.

The first episode of the first series opens with some ducks in a pond. Then it moves into a sequence that builds up to something that we've seen before, elsewhere: there is a police deputy, a harmed woman washed up on the shoreline, the blue promontory, right by the sawmill. And there's a conversation which provides one answer to the question I've just been pondering. What can't you photograph? The dead body of Laura Palmer; the deputy, Andy, just can't do it.

## Single lens reflex

The scenario, this protocol for *Twin Peaks*, is that the town doctor; Harry, the chief of police, and Deputy Andy Brennan have been called out to attend the discovery of a dead body. Andy has the camera; he's meant to take photos of the crime scene and the victim.

Here's the dialogue:

Doc: We'd better take some pictures.

Andy: Who is she?

Harry: Andy, pictures.

Andy: Sorry.

Harry: I need to turn her over.

Andy: Sure, ok. [noise of shutter release: click, click] [whimper]

Doc: Oh Andy. [Andy is weeping.]

Harry: My god, Andy. Same thing as last year in Mr Blodge's barn.

Doc: Give me the camera.

Andy: Sorry.

Harry: Is this going to happen every damn time?

Andy: I'm sorry, I'm so sorry.

Harry: Why don't you go up to the coroner's van and bring back that stretcher?

Andy: Ok. Sorry.

Doc: Harry, let's roll her over. Good lord, Laura.

Harry: Laura Palmer.

Doc: Laura.

The music swells, the tv camera moves in and remains on Laura's face, and everything kicks off for twenty-seven years. Why is Laura's body such a frosted blue, wrapped in blue plastic? Because she's dead, icy, out of the water. (It's also a precursor to a load of mystical symbolism about the blue rose, which is the name of an FBI project investigating a sinister phenomenon of the doubling of people and bodies that should not occur in nature.) But I would propose that Laura's body is also blue because it holds an echo of Michael Light's version of the Apollo 12 picture, of the astronaut "surrounded by blue aura thought to be water-vapor ice crystals." And because it's a reminder of Anna Atkins' cyanotypes, the pictures of seaweed, the liminal plants, the ones at the edge of the water, the ones that are photographed, rising up from the blue.

Andy here is a police deputy (in an artwork from 1990), who is among the first on the scene after a young woman has been killed at night, washed up into the seaweed. This makes him a double, a repeated image of his predecessor, Patrolman Len Hendricks (in *Jaws* the book from 1974). It's the same situation: sent out in the search team, finding the woman's body. Len sees Chrissie, thinks that her breast looks like a pressed flower in a memory book, and what does he do? He vomits, phytoscopically.

What does *Twin Peaks'* Andy Brennan, in his turn, do? He cries and is unable to take the photo. He can't make the image of the woman, of her body parts that his precursor thought were flower-like. Andy, what can't you take a photo of? Laura. And this isn't the first time (that's becoming obvious). Is this going to happen every time, asks Harry, who serves in Twin Peaks as the voice of order, duty, general American goodness. Yes, we can confidently answer. Every damn time.

## Take me home

There's a lot, an awful lot, in *Twin Peaks* about repetition: doubles, remakes, returns. To take one from hundreds of examples, the FBI agent hero, Cooper, is, in the third television series, replicated in at least triplicate. He is carbon-copied in a smudged sort of way, his body used to house both a dead-eyed killer and, elsewhere, a locked-in version of his familiar spirit. Then there's him floating round in space, in and out of camera mechanisms. There's him returned to vim and vigour, back to his law-enforcing self. And at the conclusion there's a weird sort of Cooper, a grim, not-particularly-appreciative-of-coffee one who ends the series with confusion, in the penultimate utterance of "What year is this?" If you're tuning in to repetition and doubles, it won't escape your notice that the penultimate exchange of *Jaws* the film is law enforcement agent Brody's splashing query, "Hey, what day is this?"

There's another, essential way in which *Twin Peaks* presents people being repeated, and that's in the way that it has unfolded over, through, time. Almost all the original actors persist, from the dead start to a quarter-century later, and of course, because the material is all on film, it can be re-spliced; the characters right at the end can watch, repeat, relive the footage from the start with their early selves in it. They can almost make it un-happen.

But the whole of *Twin Peaks: The Return* is about seeing ourselves after time has done its number. All the actors are there; we can see them back in the flower of youth, by summoning up Episode One on the streaming service, and there they are, back into as much life as an onscreen character ever was in. Then toggle to the end, and we can watch them lately as their older selves. We watch them leave, as well, with many of the episodes in *The Return* series dedicated, in the closing credits, to a particular actor who has died between filming and transmission. That's what happened in that gap: real people came to their ends, one by one. *Twin Peaks* has the actors young and it has them old, the way that time repeats us day by day, mechanically, vitally. Repetition is continuity, is life.

## Chewed up again

And repetition is of vital importance within photography; it has come to be one of the art form's defining features, although, oddly, it is not required for it. A photograph can be a unique image, unrepeatable, and there's room for philosophical debate about whether two prints from one negative are identical or not. But part of the form's huge popularity arose from just this attribute of repeatability, the idea that one negative can give innumerable prints that are all the same.

There's something interesting about the Anna Atkins *Algae* images of 1843, which is that though these are a type of photograph, they are not reproductions. Each print of a particular seaweed, rather, is a unique, not-precisely-repeated image. Schaaf (in his 1979 article on Atkins) suggests that a relatively robust bit of seaweed could be used many times without its quality deteriorating, and that Atkins would simply make one image, lift out the speci-men, place it down on the next bit of paper in as close a fashion as possible to how she'd just done it on the first; repeat at will. (And if it did get too battered and squashed, she'd have to go down to the sea again, gather another sample.) So as it is, each image of e.g. *Con-ferva linum*, in each persisting, extant version of *British Algae* might look very similar, but conceptually each cyanotype is new, distinct. The different versions are not printed from the same negative, but made anew each time; it's a different image, of the same bit of sea-weed. Atkins is prefiguring J. L. Borges' *Pierre Menard, Author of the Quixote* (first published in Spanish in 1939; in English, 1962), in which a book might look the same as an existing one, but it has come about at a different time, by a separate process.

Atkins' contemporary W. H. F. Talbot started producing his own photographic publication the following year, 1844. This was *The Pencil of Nature*, and it was unlike *Algae* in that each of the four hundred-plus copies contained photographic prints from a neg-ative. While not every print was identical, depending on circum-stances and events during each printing, they were by category, conceptually, the same.

It's a concept that theorist Walter Benjamin picks up and runs with, in his *The Work of Art in the Age of Mechanical Reproduction* of 1935 (first English translation, 1969). His discussion of repetition and the aura of the artwork is well-known. Less fêted (unaccount-ably, to my mind) is his discussion of sharks, in *Radio Benjamin*, a series for children that ran from 1927 to 1933 (there's an English-language version of the broadcasts available online via Clocktower Radio). One episode concerns bootleggers in America during Pro-hibition; in it, Benjamin tells a story of the fish men handling sharks suspiciously delicately on delivery at a restaurant, because, it turns out, each shark had a bottle of hooch shoved down its throat.

Mechanical copies and sharks? That'll lead up nicely to *Jaws* the film, in which there is a direct reference to what, before Peter Benchley, was probably the most famous explosion of the shark into popular consciousness: the 1916 East Coast attacks. It's hard to hear, because the characters are talking over each other, in anger and anxiety, but marine biologist Hooper and the police chief, Brody, splutter in concert at the mayor that "We've already had three incidents, two people killed inside of a week, and it's gonna happen again, it's happened before, the Jersey beach, right—nineteen sixteen—there were five people—five people—they were chewed up in the surf—in one week."

## Return ticket, for me and my car

Repetition, they're talking about, on both a local, immediate-time scale, and on a historical scale. Brody doesn't want this week's attacks to be repeated, and to convey the full danger he offers the occasion when the whole situation has happened before, back in New Jersey. There's also an earlier, strange comment about repetition, in the excellent ferry scene of the film. (It's filmed, with Spielbergian technical brilliance, on the real-life Chappaquiddick ferry. The scene has Brody and the mayor arguing, while Len Hendricks looks on, leaning on a magnificent Cadillac Coupe de Ville 1974, in terracotta mist.) Brody has expressed a desire to close the beaches, so that no one else might be harmed. The mayor is distinctly averse to this and argues Brody out of it. During the conversation, he proposes an alternative explanation of what happened to Chrissie: "A summer girl goes swimming, swims out a little far, she tires, a fishing boat comes along. . ." At this point the mayor's sidekick, a selectman, or, local councillor, makes a remarkable interjection: "It's happened before!"

Is he telling the truth, that swimmers have been killed and churned by boat propellers, on previous occasions? It's possible.

But he seems more carried along by a desire to back up the mayor. That's what all the selectmen have agreed to do: play down the shark angle, boost the tourism. So in the heat of the mayor's conversation, he chimes in with this reinforcing comment. It's not in the book.

There's Brody's anxious "it's gonna happen again, it's happened before." There's the selectman's interpolation: "It's happened before!" and then there's a third time in *Jaws* the film in which repetition is noted, feared, finally enacted. It's when Quint, the shark fisherman, is afraid of a wartime event repeating itself, during his speech about how his best friend died just after they had delivered the "bum, the atomic bum," as he bathetically pronounces it.

## Hull number CA-35

What's he talking about? Quint's much-admired monologue, as they carouse on his boat one night, does not derive from *Jaws* the book. Director Spielberg, in various interviews, credits writer Howard Sackler with introducing the idea for the speech; other writers adjusted and fine-tuned the final version, the purpose of which is to explain the motivation for Quint's hatred of sharks. The backstory they devised is to enlist Quint on the crew of the USS *Indianapolis*, a heavy cruiser that saw action in the Aleutians and the Pacific during World War Two.

The real history of the *Indianapolis* is this: in 1945 the ship was charged with a secret mission, to deliver to Tinian Island in the Marianas the uranium which was to be used in the Little Boy bomb which would be dropped on Hiroshima on 6th August. It set off from California hours after the Trinity test was concluded, and, arriving at Tinian on 26th July, delivered its cargo. On leaving Tinian the *Indianapolis* went to Guam, and was then en route to Leyte in the Philippines. But it never arrived, because on 30th July the ship was torpedoed by a Japanese submarine. Of the 1,195 sailors on board, three hundred went down with the ship, 316 were rescued when the navy became aware of them three days later, and in the meantime the remainder either drowned, died of other causes, or were eaten by sharks. (It was the Navy's worst loss of life at sea for a single ship; the wreckage lay undiscovered until 2017.)

That's what (the fictional) Quint says happened to his friend: they were both serving on this ship, and as they clung to wreckage, sharks ate the friend. Repetition of the *Indianapolis*—military history—is the thing that Quint fears. It's the reason he won't wear a lifejacket; he is scared of sharks biting his legs, and he would rather just drown. (It's a matter of taste whether Spielberg's decision to have Quint dying in exactly this way, legs eaten, is a subtle reference to hubris and the inevitability of fate, or a characteristic bludgeoning the viewer over the head with the obvious.) That's the imagined history for Quint, and it's what he explains, drunkenly, to Brody and Hooper as they reveal their scars, discuss lost love, look for the shark.

## Ripple all the way back

It's an interesting story for screenwriter Sackler to import into the film, for the character Quint to insert himself into. He doesn't express it like this, but Quint is claiming a role in a story in which he and his best friend, fellow sailors, have just delivered the new, never-before-used weapon that would prove decisive. The bomb would not be detonated for another week, but the process was underway, the set of actions had begun that would contribute decisively to the Americans winning the war. The sailors were on track for victory, on the home straight, when something unexpected hit them, and they were all tipped out into the water.

We've seen this set-up before. Aeschylus recounts it in the fifth century BC, how the Greeks, caught in a long war with Troy, deploy their secret and cunning weapon: the wooden horse (which is not just a decorative item but a type of wooden box with holes in it, a container, a vehicle). After the weapon has been activated, the enemy are routed and the victorious army starts returning to Greece, but there's a set-back: the storm, and the wreckage, the bloom of youth all ruined; the sea a field of corpses, bodies like flowers.

To recap: *Jaws* the film shows in Quint's death a dreaded repeat of one military event, the American ship torpedoed in the Pacific, and this 1945 sinking itself carries echoes of Aeschylus' war story, with the aftermath of victory when the water is nevertheless "flowering with corpses." So there's Aeschylus' version of death in the water, and there's screenwriter Howard Sackler's, in a film whose plot is specifically about repetition: is this going to happen every damn time, this shark attack on a human, this flowering of the corpses, like Chrissie's? Yes, it will, and it will be reiterated in *Jaws 2, Jaws 3-D, Jaws 4*, and the subsequent genre of shark films: *Sharknado*, etc. It's happened before. It keeps on coming back, "Just when you thought it was safe to go back in the water." (The inspired tagline for the 1978 sequel was dreamt up by ad-man Andrew J. Kuehn.) This has happened before. This will happen again.

All this repetition but is there an actual prototype? In my reckoning of the flowers in the water, I'm tracing it back and back to Aeschylus and what his herald says. But of course I wasn't there, I didn't directly experience it. It's just my approximate estimates of the probable truths of hypotheses (to quote from creature neuroscientist Barlow), based on the dramatic depictions of them. And it's not even a depiction but a description, a messenger's recounting, within a play that's repeated each performance, encore and encore. This gap between experience and understanding, between event and telling, is important. Of course Agamemnon's sinking is not photographic as such, but it raises the idea of the delay, the pause in which we wait for the re-visioning of an event, wait for the herald, wait for the image to arrive. Such a delay is central to photography, and I think that photography allows us to consider the question of delay in a way that is then useful for understanding it in other arenas: in literature, in personal and broader history, in our sense of self.

If you ask, with Brody or with the audience to a Greek tragedy, what's the cause/reason, it's always, well, something happened before. Whatever the original was, it's down there on the ocean floor just beyond our line of vision. The light refracts and bends on the way from it to us. All we can get, along with Anna Atkins, are the shadows of the traces of the copies of the objects that have drifted to the surface. Or, like Michael Light, we might try to pursue the original down there, among the wreckage. But it's dark, mystifying, three-martini disorientating, it's all in reverse, negative; and there are sharks. Most of the time, something might have happened, but we only see the after-effects; the shockwaves just keep on coming. All our lives.

# EXPLOSIONS

*nitro*

*Nitroglycerine*—violently explosive substance, yellowish oily liquid in form, obtained from adding glycerine to a mixture of nitric and sulphuric acids.

Also in other cases, *nitro*—denoting a combination of nitric with an organic acid.

*Nitrogen* is related to these compounds (chemical and lexographic), being "that which produces nitric acid and nitrates;" it's an element, atomic number 7, that's an essential part of all life systems.

*Nitrocellulose* or nitrate film, made by exposing cellulose to sulphuric acid and potassium nitrate, was used as the first flexible film base. Due to its propensity to burst into flames and burn down cinemas, it was replaced, first by cellulose acetate or safety film, then by polyester film.

## Books on sharks

We know that *Jaws* the film (denouement for the shark: explosion by Hooper's gas canisters of compressed air—mainly oxygen and nitrogen) has its precursors, and that one line of descent is naval-historical; it follows in the wake of previous battles at sea. Its other lineage is literary; it follows in the wake of *Jaws* the book. But what does that, in turn, derive from? What is jawsogenic (to apply the suffix as it's used in scientific terminology), what is the cause of *Jaws*?

It's happened before, in 1916, splutters Brody in the film, of the shark attacks. But it's not just fish that circle round and come back, it's books, too. I'm particularly interested in comparing Benchley's story about sharks, from 1974, with a book that fixates on the 1916 events, and that appeared not long before he was writing: *Shadows in the Sea: The Sharks, Skates and Rays*, from 1963, published by Weathervane Books. I'm sure this was a source of inspiration and information for Benchley, who was a reporter and an East Coast resident, well-read and able to research, and likely to be familiar with one of the most important, and local, incidents in the literature.

*Shadows* is a wonderful book, co-written by three authors. Headlining, and most vocally present in the text, is Harold McCormick, fishing enthusiast, who works for the Board of Education. His mentor is grizzled sea dog Captain William Young, who, although he dies before publication, provides the lifetime's experience. Quietest of the triumvirate is newspaperman Tom Allen, who seems to do the actual work of gathering information, amassing content, pulling the book into shape. They are the Quint-Hooper-Brody of shark textbook compilation. The book is a mine of information. It's strong on paleontology—the clues from history, from the bodies buried in stone—and has an extremely thorough chapter on "Sharks and their Allies in Mythology, Legend, Folklore, and Crime," which includes tales from around the world, and legal cases ranging from blockade-breaking to murder. Sharks get everywhere.

## Rub up against the other

McCormick is most keen, though, on the shark-human interface. Of the four parts to his book, the first three are entitled "Shark against Man," "Man against Shark," and, "Man and Shark." I love this book because it is struggling towards a broader philosophical point than it knows how to express. In his fascination with sharks and killing them, McCormick tries to explain something about his own place in the world, through the making of stories, and the listening to the word-of-mouth experiences of people who've come before. There's something extraordinary that is much, much bigger than him, but instead of ignoring, fleeing it, he dares to investigate, to try to understand. I find him admirable (if not admiral), despite his "Appendix: Selachian Cookery" (*selachian*: of the shark kind; *elasmobranch*: shark). In the foreword he states:

> At one point, we compiled a list of factors and conditions which seemingly would encourage a shark attack. It was a long list. We decided not to print it because, we realized, the list was based on *human* thinking and not on whatever goes on in the brain of the shark.

He's decentralizing his own assumptions here, and channeling Michel de Montaigne: *que sçais-je*, what do I know?

## To philosophize is to learn how to swim

The opening chapter of *Shadows* is dedicated to revitalizing the story of the 1916 shark encounters on the east coast of the U.S.A. To get his information, McCormick trawled through newspaper articles from the time, then interviewed witnesses to the attacks. The resulting account is a tour de force, with its historical positioning, the turns of phrase, the little details.

The story is, that in 1916, while the still-mysterious polio was ravaging New York and entry into the First World War was imminent, American holiday-makers were glad to escape to the beaches for their summer holidays. But a spate of fatal shark attacks caused uproar. Two swimmers at two different beaches were killed, followed by a boy who was frolicking inland in a creek, and the young man who tried to rescue him. One further boy, downriver, had his leg bitten off. Shark experts downplayed, then admitted to, the seriousness of the situation. There was a media mêlée, and attempts to catch the shark, of doubtful success. Then, in a frenzy of shark-hunters, newspaper headlines, dynamite (local stores sold out), and hysteria, the shark menace was gone. Four dead, one injured. That's McCormick's account, his historical record written in 1963.

Four dead, one bitten—you can see the influence of this on *Jaws* the book, of 1974. Definitely eaten: swimmer Chrissie, little Alex Kintner, Morris Cater (as shockingly witnessed by Patrolman Len Hendricks), then Hooper in the final act. Fisherman Ben Gardner disappears off his boat, the presumed perpetrator leaving as carte-de-visite an enormous, serrated tooth embedded in the gunwale. Jim Prescott, teenager, accepts a dare to swim for the benefit of a tv crew, but he comes out pretty damn quickly when the shark starts to chase him. Quint is pulled into the water by the harpoon rope, not bitten but drowning as he dangles just yards in front of the shark's teeth. That's it. Four confirmed shark deaths, one pretty certain. One teenage near miss; one drowning. One heroic survivor.

Who dies in *Jaws* the film, of 1975? Four people on camera—Chrissie, Alex, a nameless man in the pond, Quint—and one off-screen (fisherman Ben Gardner). There are variations, substitutions, but we can trace a clear thread between the three instances of attack: McCormick's historical yarn, Benchley's book, and Spielberg's film. This is not unusual; writing is about retelling.

## What's up, Werther?

What else happens in the translation, the gap, between *Shadows* then *Jaws* the book and *Jaws* the film? I'm greatly entertained by cultural theorist Fredric Jameson's 1979 reading ("Reification and Utopia in Mass Culture," in the journal *Social Text*), in which he expresses surprise that the vast American audience for *Jaws* the film is not more disappointed by the fact that Hooper survives, given that this deviates from the classic Romantic heroic trope (as seen in the book) of a suicidal young man giving himself to the sublime. I think Jameson overestimates how much the average 1970s cinema-goer cares, about the Romantic sublime.

But I'm also interested in something that was in place long before the motion picture. During McCormick's chapter about the famous set of shark attacks, there is a strand that keeps emerging or poking a fin up, about technologies of vision, about perception. I'll go through some of his description of the summer, pointing out this presence, suggesting what it might tell us about looking at the cataclysm.

## Optical technology

The account in *Shadows* of the first victim is relatively straightforward: Charles Van Sant was impatient to get into the water for his first swim of the holiday at Beach Haven, New Jersey; "Time had been too slow for him." As he happily swam, onlookers saw "a gray shadow" rapidly approach, then he was bitten, pulled out of the water, died.

The second victim was (another namesake) Charles Bruder, a bellboy at the fashionable resort of Spring Lake, New Jersey. He went out to swim but there was a kerfuffle. As McCormick tells it, Bruder disappeared and, " 'He has upset!' the woman screamed. 'The man in the red canoe is upset!' " The lifeguards ran to their rescue boat. "They knew that it was not the reflection of an over-turned canoe they saw, for even now the red blot was spreading, and in the midst of it, for one awful moment, Bruder's agonized face appeared, and he flung up a bloodied arm." Watching from a hotel balcony was a society lady. "She turned to her maid and asked for her spyglass."

This incident of Bruder's death is an interesting example of dis-placed and deferred interpretation. The woman on the beach sees and exclaims about a man in a red canoe, because that is her im-mediate perception of the scene in front of her. But the lifeguards, and the writer, and the society dame with her telescope, know that the stretch of red on the water's surface, with half a body rising above it, is not a canoe but a pool, an outpouring of blood.

## He is dead. No doubt about it.

How do they know this, how might they know; is their actual line of sight unimpeded, have they better vision? Or is it a matter of inter-pretation, perception, having a clearer grasp of what they mean, these things that we can see? It's a literary technique of delayed decoding, as outlined by Ian Watt (see his 1979 work, published by University of California Press, *Conrad in the Nineteenth Century*, about little sticks flying through the air in *Heart of Darkness* and a man in a boat falls down. Joseph Conrad is obviously a foundational figure in the water-death-writing category). Someone there at the scene, witness or narrator, does not immediately perceive what is hap-pening; the meaning doesn't kick in until later, when further men-tal processing has taken place.

I appreciate this idea of delayed decoding, and I like books where it's used to good effect, but I can't help thinking that the idea

Electrotype illustration of *Rhodophyllis bifida*, plate 71 from *The Nature-printed British Sea-weeds, vol. II*, by Johnstone and Croall, England, 1859.

"This appears to be an ocean weed," they say.

doesn't go far enough. Because, isn't all reading and perception an ongoing process of later reinterpretation? There is further decoding every next page, and each time we think about an event or a book; there's a different understanding all the way through time as our frame of reference shifts, as we realign the digging, reconsider artifacts. We're always understanding too late, re-decoding, looking at the picture more carefully from the balcony through our spyglasses.

I'd also compare this delayed decoding process to the concept of the latent image in photography. Here's a red canoe, says the witness on the beach, implying that nothing in the scene is out of the ordinary. All is as we expect it to be, it has not changed from its initial outlook. This situation is like a photographic negative exposed to the light, and nothing appears to have happened to it; it doesn't look any different from its normal, original state. But! in the next sentence, and a few seconds later, the lifeguards have got the point, they apply their stronger understanding, and McCormick explains to the reader the true image, that Bruder's been bitten in half. This second state, of action and comprehension, is the equivalent of after the developing process, when the actual picture emerges to be fixed. It's the point when we move from apparently untouched, original scene, to the position when the true picture is clear and visible. It didn't take long, but there was a distinct gap, the time of latency, between the red canoe and the desperate, comprehending rescue dash; between the reader's first exposure to the scene, and the scene's proper representation. The latent image was there, but time plays a role, in our understanding. We need the delay.

### They're coming inland

The third and fourth victims, as described in *Shadows*, go together. They are not on the eastern seaboard but inshore, up the creek at Matawan, New Jersey. The river here drains into Raritan Bay, which in turn goes to Lower Bay, in the New York Harbour purview. The local boys like swimming and jumping in the creek. One of them, fifty years later, is interviewed by McCormick, and can show him the scars where a large, dark shape brushed against him, causing consternation. He has the proof of the past written, palimpsested, right there on his body. His eye-witness account of the deathly afternoon is backed up, underwritten, by the actual indelible marks on his skin. They'll never come off, you know.

## Nail 'em up

The story that McCormick's interlocutor tells, or proves, is this: Lester Stilwell was a local boy of twelve who had the afternoon to play, after a morning's work at his father's sawmill. He was particularly skilled at nailing up wooden boxes. He went swimming with companions (including the lucky-escape one) in the creek, where the shark ate him. Stanley Fisher, twice Stilwell's age, was also a resident. Although his father had led a seagoing life, Stanley turned down the ocean for an onshore career, setting up a dry cleaning store. It didn't do him any good. When Stanley heard of the attack on Lester, he rushed to the scene and heroically dived into the muddy creek, where he himself was bitten. Despite his injuries, he managed to claim that he had wrested the boy's body from the shark's jaws. Bystanders tried to get him to the hospital—"he lay on the baggage car waiting for death and the 5: 06"—but they were too late.

Strangely, earlier that month a customer had bought a suit from Stanley, and instead of paying cash he bartered to Stanley a life insurance policy. With the payout from that policy, his family donated to the local church a stained glass window: "the rays of the setting sun would filter through the window as day's end came to the little town of Matawan."

These are uncanny details, within a documentary-style re-counting of a shark attack. Whoever the nameless customer of Stanley's was, he reminds me of the shady figure in folk tales, pursuing the target everywhere, however you might try to evade. I picture: fresh from handing out spyglasses to see the dead swimmer, a stranger turns up in Matawan. He goes by the dry cleaners, looking for an outfit, black. Cash or charge? Neither, I'll just give you this token that reminds you that it comes to all of us sooner or later. Sooner, really, and you'll be able to exchange this token for glass that directs the sunlight in a particular pattern. Then on to the sawmill goes the stranger, asking if they can make their wooden boxes in a particular size. About six feet by two, one deep, should do. And another one, same shape, slightly smaller. You want boxes made up like a couple of coffins? Yes, and maybe a third box, just a small one, twenty by twenty by forty centimeters. The size of an old-fashioned camera.

This is the aspect that I imagine as a sort of underlay (like the cellulose base sits under the silver emulsion on a camera film), the strange story buried beneath the shark story that McCormick tells: Death coming to town, visiting the sawmill where the wooden boxes are made, sliding little parts of optics, and snatches of time, into the scene. McCormick doesn't go as far as to mention, exactly, the word "camera." But the idea is there, all the components, of wooden boxes with a lens set in, for making images. McCormick does not say, "photograph," but he's certainly pointing that way, pointing at the camera.

## What do we keep in wooden boxes?

In Hergé's underground tombs of Kih-Oskh (in *Cigars of the Pharaoh*, colour, book version first in French, 1955; English translation, 1971), we use wooden boxes to keep scores of Egyptologists, and cigars. On board the *Pequod* we keep clothes and our harpoon, now that we have remembered an outstanding duty and are no longer ready to succumb to illness (and we decorate the box by repeating the pattern from our tattoos). Queequeg (for it is he, in Herman Melville's 1851 *Moby-Dick*) admires "certain little canoes of dark wood" from Nantucket. He thinks they are canoes because of their appearance and format, like the ones that his compatriots sail off in through the starry waters after they die. Ishmael knows, but does not explain to Queequeg or to the reader, that the Nantucket boxes are coffins, for burying rather than for sailing in. We'll have to do our own decoding, for that.

We put in wooden boxes paper that has been made ready with chemicals, so it is receptive to stimulation by light waves, and will undergo change that allows it to retain an image. We keep wine bottles in wooden boxes, until the vehicle is repurposed to be Roger Fenton's travelling photographic studio in Crimea. We keep a hidden portion of the Greek army, overnight, outside the gates of the city, in a special, horse-shaped box.

Thinking back to the Lumière brothers and their innovations in colour photography, they have a delightful album of pictures they made in the first couple of decades of the twentieth century, of their home and families. There are lush gardens and large lunches outdoors. *Natures mortes*. A surprising zeppelin or dirigible over a meadow. And a couple of pictures of one of their nieces, Louloune (aged around eight, so this is circa 1912), as she plays round the gardens, then poses happily inside a big, wooden box. She's quite all right, happy and healthy, nothing to do with the Victorian trend for photographic perpetuating of babies who had died. Except, of course, Louloune is now dead, long buried in her box. Though we have her in the photo.

There is also a type of box that does not have a lid. It could do, for travelling, but usually the box is for containment without sacrificing easy access and visibility. In this we keep shaped metal type letters, upper and lower case, or sometimes butterflies, or shells and creatures. A display case, a box divided up into sections.

It seems to me that all these wooden boxes, along with their lenses, are both strongly related to cameras and are containers of death.

## CCA, Container Corporation of America

I'm greatly taken by the wooden box both because that's the format of proto-cameras, and as an item in itself, one which ties in to this nexus of war, art, image, death, that fascinates me. And although its relative or derivative the cardboard box might sound like an unpromising line of enquiry, well, everything can contain good stories, if you look carefully inside. I became interested in the American businessman Walter Paepcke (born 29th June 1896, died 13th April 1960), who made a fortune out of, first, wooden boxes, then boxes made out of cardboard, or, (in American English) paperboard.

Like the Stilwells in Matawan, who lost their little boy to a shark, and the fictional Packards of *Twin Peaks*, Paepcke was from a sawmill family. He inherited his family's firm, the Chicago Mill and Lumber Company, which specialized in turning trees into wooden boxes. He merged this into his new business, Container Corporation of America, set up in 1926, and shifted the emphasis into making packaging out of cardboard, instead. CCA was a hugely successful company for many decades (though it has now been engulfed by waves of corporate cannibalism and restructuring) and Walter and his wife, the designer Elizabeth Nitze Paepcke (born, 28th August 1902, died June 1994), became munificently wealthy. Like Walter, Elizabeth was from a European immigrant background, her father and brother a diplomat and eminent academic, respectively.

The urbane Paepckes offered support and employment to Bauhaus designers who fled Europe during the 1930s; they played a role in cultivating their hometown of Chicago as a serious base for art and design; and they even took the trouble to organize the Goethe Bicentennial Festival in Aspen, Colorado, in 1949. In work as well as in their personal and philanthropic activities, the Paepckes were evangelists for contemporary art and graphic design, most famously through CCA's advertising campaigns, which became a byword for ambition and excellence.

## Billions of powdered eggs

The Smithsonian American Art Museum holds a wonderful collection of CCA work, which includes both advertising material and works on (of course) paper from the corporate art collection. From the late 1930s, the advertising artwork was provided by a breathtaking roster of serious artists: Fernand Léger, A. M. Cassandre, Man Ray, all illustrating the virtues of cardboard.

America's entry into war increased demand for packaging, and alongside this CCA's ad campaigns stepped up a gear, too. There's a fascinating mixture, within the images destined for trade and consumer print magazines, of practical messaging and abstraction. Cardboard is useful; it's a good protective substance for transporting materiel and food. But the work is also dizzyingly abstract, wider-picture: cardboard is presented as part of a cosmic cycle of growth, processing, struggle, human consciousness. There's a pleasing awareness of metaphorical ambiguity in the war effort slogans of "Can Paperboard Stop a Shell?", "Paperboard Saves Metal," "Paperboard Packs a Mighty Wallop," and "Paperboard Fills the Soldier's Pack." And even a touch of surrealism, in collage-style images of troops protected by virtue of forming the folding sides of a cardboard box.

In two subsequent campaigns depicting Allied nations, and the states of the U.S., the balance tipped further towards the abstract. Cardboard went by the wayside, and the essence of each geographical entity was conveyed via mainly not-straighforwardly-representational images. All this led up to the later, and longest-lasting campaign, which ran with the idea that what CCA should be peddling was not a product but the very ethos of the company. And the company ethos was expansive.

## From sawmills to the Smithsonian

Influenced by attendance at a University of Chicago reading group that considered a corpus of literature in the Western canon, Elizabeth Paepcke pushed for a CCA campaign based on a parallel premise: not great whole books but great ideas. Each advertisement would consist of a quotation—up to a short paragraph from literature, politics, science, or philosophy, from a source chosen by her committee—which would be offered to a contemporary artist as a prompt to produce any image he or she wanted, in response. Running from February 1950 (with a quotation from Alexander Hamilton, art by Arthur Williams) until the 1980s, this *Great Ideas of Western Man* campaign included contributions from really quite a roll call of artists: Philip Guston, Leo Lionni, René Magritte, Pauline Boty, Saul Bass, Corita Kent, and hundreds more.

It's an excellent series, which indicates what ideas were held in high esteem (the series began as ". . . of Western Man;" Elizabeth Paepcke added "Eastern Man" in 1957; sadly, no-one added "Women"); which showcases a great range of mid-twentieth-century artists; and which was highly influential as an ad campaign. It's well worth perusing. There are grand political statements, high-minded ideas about humanity, lines of poetry, and artworks that you wouldn't normally see, all set in unexpected pairings. Each finished page of advertisement has: the text and the art, the name of the writer and of the artist, and the name and logo of CCA. There is nothing at all, at any time, about the product, cardboard—that wasn't the point.

For example, from 1966 there is an ad that consists of John Massey's abstract, collage-like leaf, overlaid with two blocks of reversed, negative colours. There are three small notches in the middle of the leaf, like cricket stumps. And above the image, up in the top right corner of the page, there are the first two sentences of Dylan Thomas' 1933 (in a poetry magazine; 1934 in the book *18 Poems*) first-line-entitled work, this great, very Thomassy poem, about language, water, time, and death:

> The force that through the green fuse drives the flower
> Drives my green age; that blasts the roots of trees
> Is my destroyer.

Thomas here is yet another person echoing Aeschylus and the herald's report on the returning Aegean army, his imagery ranging from the flower to the blasted tree, from youth and love to death. It's pleasing to see all these large themes—language, life force, explosions—appearing in just one of CCA's ads for cardboard boxes. They contain multitudes, indeed.

I like the way that imagery of Agamemnon surrounded in the water by the flowering corpses keeps coming back, a ghost or blur on so many images. I can see him in Thomas' poem, found in the museum archive of Container Corporation of America; in Quint's yarn where he inserts himself into the *Indianapolis* in *Jaws* the film; in Laura Palmer, washed up like an icy blue flower on the shores of Twin Peaks, where she can't be properly photographed. I see him in all the photographs that could be taken of flowers, from Anna Atkins' haunting, lovely shapes in the blue, to all the other images made out of the silver salts, which leave their blue traces down on the bones, their marks like flowers on the skin.

Of course Agamemnon keeps on coming home. He himself is not one of the drowned sailors out of the returning, victorious army who dies in the storm, in among the *ereipiois*, the wreckage; he survives and makes it all the way back. And then what? His wife, Clytemnestra, gets her vengeance, starting by laying out the purple cloths beneath his feet to welcome him home; like any good photographer, she has an idea planned that will develop in the silvered bath.

## ACC / CCA; Alfred Capel Cure / Canadian Centre for Architecture

Images, destruction, flowers, invention: photo, nitro, phyto, proto. They keep coming back. There's a final photographer I'd like to consider, who, as we'll see, has a connection to Dylan Thomas' poem, and to these four words of compound or prefix that have seeded themselves through this work. It's Alfred Capel Cure, a professional soldier and amateur photographer who was born in 1826. He enjoyed a wealthy upbringing: time to pursue artistic pursuits, a summer residence in Gibraltar, that sort of thing. One uncle, Edward Cheney, was a Grand Tour type who lived part of the time in Venice, and amassed there a nice collection of Tiepolos. Alfred's father was a military man, with Alfred and siblings growing up in the family home of Blake Hall, Essex, which is still owned by Capel Cures.

Blake Hall is in London, just about. You go far north-east, past Chigwell, out to the countryside. You used to be able to get there on the tube (the London Underground) but it dropped off the map in 1981. Blake Hall, the grand house itself, is still there, but the station that the landowner had insisted upon is no longer used. And it was never actually underground, but in daylight, among fields. A phototropic station. There are various tube stations that have become defunct, ghostly like this, and they inspire a certain loyalty or fascination, among Londoners. It's not (not usually) that a place disappears, is blasted to oblivion; rather, a neighbourhood is considered surplus to requirements. Sometimes a station on the periphery leaves the orbit, is grafted onto another network, reconfigured into a different line. Sometimes it is allowed to fade away, the metal removed and the weeds left to grow over. There will be marks left, though, shadows on the surface, for later archaeologists. And we still have the maps, showing the image of the pattern, the decorative picture of the system.

Through unmarried uncles on his mother's side, Alfred Capel Cure also spent much time at the Cheney family home at Badger Hall, Shropshire (this was actually demolished, in 1953). It was here, with another uncle, Robert Henry Cheney, that Alfred took to the recent craze for photography in a big way. It's hard to tell from their output who did what, but they maintained the hobby vigorously through the decade of the 1850s, mainly using the calotype process and collecting the prints in albums for personal use; they did not exhibit or sell works.

Capel Cure's photography can be divided into three main strands. There are pictures of soldiers, whom he encountered during his twenty-three years in the army, joining in 1844. There are architectural studies, of Rievaulx Abbey, Corfe Castle, tumbledown churches, all in keeping with the ruins aesthetic that informed plenty of mid-nineteenth-century art. And there are domestic scenes, though domestic-external rather than indoors, of his life and environment in the two family possessions of Badger Hall and Blake Hall—nephews, family dogs, servants at work.

Soldiers, architecture, and gardens. Explosions, blueprints, flowers. Nitro, proto, phyto. (It's the second group, architectural studies, that would explain why the institution with the largest collection of Capel Cure's work today is the Canadian Centre for Architecture, Montreal—the CCA. They hyphenate his surname, which not everyone does. His work is also held by the Getty, MoMA, the Metropolitan Museum of Art.) I'd like to discuss a couple, or some couples, of his images further.

## The wreck and ruin of a noble man

The first is Capel Cure's photograph of an oak tree that has been struck by lightning. This is one set-up, but there are two distinct examples of it, from two separate years. It might be that trees were just a convenient subject for Capel Cure, as they were too for Talbot and other contemporaries. A tree is handy to depict because it doesn't move much, it's outdoors where the light is best, it's easily recognizable but interestingly sculptural, etc. But two separate versions of an oak struck by lightning? If we're seeing double, it's worth looking closer. It's slightly tricky to disentangle, as there are several different prints of two different exposures, and the institutions that hold each print refer to them by different names. But basically, two trees in England, struck during two different storms.

The second example, according to MoMA, is *Tree Struck by Lightning, Hill Hall, Essex*, dated to March 1858. (Hill Hall is not Capel Cure's home itself, but a neighbouring estate.) The CCA calls its version of this *A Blasted Oak, Hill Hall*, and written on the page just under the title is the date, "13 May 58," and "Some fragments, at 55 yards from the tree."

The other photograph is two years older, from 1856. The Met lists it as *Oak Struck by Lightning, Badger*, while the CCA transcribes slightly messy handwriting on the mount to call it *Oak Struck by Lighteningar Snowden Pool, Badger Hall; 11<sup>th</sup> Dec 1856*. A photo with a third name, *Split Tree at Badger Hall*, was sold at Sotheby's in London in the sale "Fine Photographs from the Collection of Paul F. Walter" in May 2001 (Walter was a curator at MoMA). There were two Capel Cure photos included in this sale, and while a picture of Wells Cathedral went for double its estimate, this *Split Tree* sold for twenty-two thousand pounds, or seven times its estimate; it seems it was the particular photo, not the photographer in general, that was so sought-after.

## Homesick blues

The later-dated photo, of the struck tree at Hill Hall in Essex in 1858, is the busier, more complex of the two. It shows a tree with its top section struck off, but the tree is still filling the top half of the print with dark branches, and the bottom half with silvered ones. It's like a Jackson Pollock, with the rhythm of the lines, the light and dark over the white sky or the black ground. There are parts where the tree has turned out on itself, the inside of its trunk now exposed, and the branches also mark out space through the air, a complex pattern like a knotted tangle in a ball of wool. If you follow a twig in, it's like entering into the maze, following your path through space back to the centre. There's also what looks like a hedge behind, and grass underneath at the front of the space, which offers more visual noise.

The 1856 Badger split tree, by contrast, is seen from further away; the camera isn't in among the tangle of branches. It's one tree against plain white sky, and a more consistent field floor. And it's easy to note the shape: the trunk rises cleanly, but it has been hit and cleaved into two matching halves, one lurching forward to the bottom right of the frame, one leaning back to the middle left. It's a neat bit of damage and devastation, rather than the messy profusion of the Essex tree.

Roger Taylor in *Impressed by Light* suggests of this 1856 photo by Capel Cure that

> Perhaps he saw the awkwardly arching limbs and shattered form of this young oak struck by lightning as an analogue for the agonies he had witnessed during the Crimean War, when so many colleagues and friends in his regiment were torn apart by shot and shell. This death portrait of a tree was made almost exactly

Alfred Capel-Cure, *A Blasted Oak, Hill Hall*, albumen silver print, 1858.

This is the second of the Capel Cure iterations of a lightning-struck tree, in the Canadian Centre for Architecture version. MoMA only shows it online, cropped to the image itself, no surrounds.

a year after he was severely wounded and nearly lost his life leading his men successfully into battle during the siege of Sebastopol.

Taylor is chanelling Dylan Thomas here, wondering if the force that blasts the roots of trees is Capel Cure's destroyer. Perhaps. It's hard to say. Taylor's referring to Capel Cure's experiences in Crimea, where the British and allied armies over the summer of 1855 finally took the fortifications and the town of Sebastopol: a decisive point of the war (the Russians lost). At the third attempt in September, the British succeeded in storming the Great Redan. This was part of the defences that the Russians had built along the Malakov ridge of hills, to the south of the town. They had dug and reinforced, rearranging the landscape into protective shape, and one form of such earthworks is the "redan," two walls of earth meeting at a jutting-out angle. The word comes from the French *dent*, for "tooth," and comes from the fact that a redan forms a point, like the triangular tooth of a saw. Or a shark.

## Not single spies but in battalions

There's another image made by Capel Cure that I'd like to consider, beyond his blasted oak trees. It's a photograph that art historian Geoffrey Batchen describes in *Photography at MoMA 1840–1920* as "one of the stranger images from the nineteenth century to have survived." This image is *My Beasts*, a waxed paper negative exposed on 1st February 1852. It is an odd artwork.

It shows a wooden box, containing creatures: mainly moths. Or butterflies—I can't tell, because they appear only as whited-out shapes, with just a few of the forty-odd revealing any mark or pattern on the wings. The others I suppose could be identified by shape alone, by a hotshot lepidopterist. There is also a seahorse, a centipede-type thing, a stag beetle, what looks like a tiny newt?

I think the creatures are in a display case. Again, it's hard to distinguish, because it's in negative. These white shapes are arrayed, wings open, against a black rectangle, which has hanging loops and a string. I can't see any sign of pins fastening the specimens to a board. They must be dead—live creatures wouldn't stay still, wouldn't allow themselves to be collected like this, into a type case or wooden box. So maybe they are glued on, or it could be that they are laid flat on a horizontal surface, and that's how they are not falling off. Except that the board or case has a string attached, which rises in a triangle to a point off the top of the frame of the image. It's a shape that visually suggests a case hanging from a nail. And, there's a ghost trail of whiteness on this negative, behind the board and the string, showing where, in the real room, a light source behind the photographer's shoulder was casting a shadow.

Behind the darkest rectangle of the case, the background of the image is lighter, a pleasant, dusty shade of almost-purple. Down in the lower left there is a white, verging-on-orange globule that looks like a blob of guano. Why would my mind turn to images of guano? Because standing on top of the display case, arms outstretched, is a large bat! It's not in the display case, put in there by the collector or photographer, but looming right over, guarding, presenting this case full of the fellow creatures.

Or perhaps the bat is addressing all the moths (and irregulars) in the box, who are there, attentive, heads up towards this leader. Or it's lamenting them, trying to enfold all its dead comrades up in an embrace. Who knows. Who knows why Capel Cure in 1852, before his war service and his injury, has this image straight out of someone's nightmare subconscious, these nocturnal things of darkness all ready to advance out of their collection case, following their bat-leader as it calls out the title, *My Beasts*.

Then one more strange detail on a strange picture. Above the bat, blurring at the top centre of the image, where the hanging strings meet in a capital A, there is a patch of whiteness that looks like a mass of seaweed. Like fronds, edging downwards, the spiky, straight-line, dendrite type. Can it be seaweed, set into the picture? It would make scarcely less sense than having a large bat overseeing a collection of moths. But maybe it's a flaw in the taking, a sneaky intrusion of light into the process. Or a problem with the chemicals on the paper, a stain or poor concentration that results in a lighter patch. The shape is slightly smeared, like a cloud, but at its edges it fractures out, branching into lines. The shape resembles cracks on a mirror, cracks formed not so much by the glass cracking, but from the silver behind the glass blotching and pooling black, with time. Like the melanin spreading over Kuchnow's lemon shark's guanine platelets.

## Now you see me

Alfred Capel Cure was born in 1826 and joined the army at eighteen. The historian Roger Taylor explains that Capel Cure arrived in the Crimea on 5th June 1855 and was plunged straight into action. He led the storming of the Quarries at Sebastopol, and then took temporary command of his regiment, as so many senior officers had died. In September, severely wounded, he was sent home to recuperate. From the next year, 1856, among his albums and works there are two self-portraits. One (it's on the Met's website) shows him in brevet lieutenant uniform, stylish wide-leg trousers, looking mutton-chopped but not particularly damaged, facing into the camera with a self-aware expression. He's leaning on the pediment of a low stone wall which is topped by a huge stone vase, empty of flowers, and the vase appears to be decorated with two little ornamental heads. These heads are not of nymphs but of a moustachio'd male figure. Unusual.

In the second photo (from the collection of the Charles E. Young Research Library; in Taylor's *Impressed by Light*), dated more precisely to the 29th September, Capel Cure is in mufti. He stands at the right of the frame in the very same pose, leaning his weight on a straight left leg with his right arm stretched down. But here his left hand is curled round a string rather than round the pommel of his sword. His right hand now is resting on what are presumably photo albums, while across from him, staring right at him, is a camera on elegant tripod legs. (A quick double-take to establish that he can't be taking the picture using the camera that appears within the photo.) Instead of standing upright in front of some impressive statuary, in the civilian photo Capel Cure is leaning on a doorframe, his right leg bent behind him, and against the blackness of the aperture you look twice to see if his leg is folded into shadow, or if it's missing. Seen in stereo, these two images of Capel Cure, soldier and photographer, with two stone mise-en-abyme miniatures of him included, have a bizarrely modern, Cindy-Sherman-esque feel. And he's looking right at us, twice, through all this time. Then also from 1856 there's the first of the blasted tree images.

Capel Cure stopped taking pictures in 1860. Taylor in a footnote states that "A study of Blake Hall, *My Last Photo, ACC, 1860*, concludes the Cure album owned by the Museum of Modern Art," but this is unavailable online. One of the press releases for MoMA's 1981 exhibition of Capel Cure refers to his diaries lacking any mention of photography, but again, I do not know who holds such diaries. But all the collections seem to agree that Capel Cure stopped all photography in 1860. He bought himself out of the army in 1867, inherited Badger Hall in 1884, and died twelve years later, in an accident. The *Globe and Traveller* newspaper of 31st July 1896 reports that:

> Colonel Alfred Capel Cure, of Badger Hall, Salop, who has been killed by the accidental explosion of dynamite with which he was going to blow up a tree, was a Crimean veteran, and was 70 years of age. He was present at Sebastopol, commanded a party of the

55$^{th}$ at the attack on the Quarries, and commanded the regiment from the middle of June to September 8, including the attacks on the Redan of June 18 and September 8. He was severely wounded. Afterwards he became a colonel of the Grenadier Guards, and retired in 1867.

## I have myself been blasted in these hopes

Dynamiting trees! This is, now, an unusual way to die. In my social circles, at least. Not so much so in his era, for a landed gentry type. The problem with a misplaced or unstable tree is that even after you chop it down with an axe or chainsaw it doesn't really go; it hangs on in there, preparing to re-gather strength (draw up nitrogen proteins through the green fuse?), preparing to put forth new growth, begin again afresh, sometime next year in the spring. To get rid of every trace, to stop the new flowers, you need to actually pulverize and extract the roots.

Capel Cure was dynamiting his trees; at first I thought that perhaps he could have devised some sort of home-made, nitrogen-based fertilizer bomb for the task. But no such thing would have been available to him in 1896. These days it is "absurdly easy" to make a home-made bomb (asserts C. W. Kauffman, an explosives expert at the University of Michigan, quoted in the *Washington Post*, 21$^{st}$ April 1995): you mix together ammonium nitrate (from fertilizer) with some petroleum-based oil and detonate it with a little dynamite. But in Capel Cure's time these ingredients were not to hand; it was not until the 1910 Haber-Bosch discovery of how to react nitrogen from the air that ammonium nitrite became commonly available. Capel Cure and his gardeners, working round the estate, would have had to use a different sort of fertilizer to add nitrogen to the plants, something more organic, containing manure or guano. They'd have kept separately the dynamite, for explosions.

## Bang up to date

Dynamite itself was a relatively new invention in the 1890s, super-seding the older, lower-impact explosive of gunpowder. Invented by Alfred Nobel, and patented in England in 1867 (the year Capel Cure left the army), dynamite consists of nitroglycerine soaked into an absorbent surrounding. Nobel didn't invent nitroglycerine, but one of the creative Swede's innovations was the discovery of how to produce it; another was the blasting cap, used to detonate a chunk. But a third problem to solve was that of how to stop the highly volatile nitroglycerine from exploding before time. Nobel tried various stabilizing substances, and the best solution he came up with, and patented, was diatomaceous earth. Which is, a pow-der made from the remains of diatoms, or, fossilized algae. Algae, like seaweed. Seaweed gives diatoms, which give dynamite.

Some substances keep appearing in, washing up on the shore of, this investigation. Seaweed is one, and it helps to make dyna-mite. Guano is another, and in parallel destructive use, it can be used in the manufacture of gunpowder. You soak the bat guano to obtain potassium nitrate crystals, then combine these to make gunpowder. Or, from guano you can extract guanine (one of the DNA building blocks of life) which is also the silvery material lin-ing the platelets at the back of the lemon shark's eye, regulating its appreciation of light. Guanine, which Kuchnow measures in his shark/photography set-up, when he matches the silvery guanine to the silver halide on the film negative.

We keep seeing silvery photographs and the wooden boxes used to obtain them. And we keep seeing flowers that appear in unexpected places: growing on blasted rubble, flashing into a trau-matised patrolman's imagination, on the title page of a collec-tion of emblem-poems. Growing where it seemed that all civiliza-tion was ruined. Everything knots together: the sharks, photos, seaweed and flower images, explosive substances. They are made from each other, of each other, cycling around, like time, which endeth where it first began. Time is the one essential component we can't depict, though it's there, at the heart, all along. *That's* what you can't photograph, though it's the only thing that makes the photograph. It's there and not there, positive, negative. The clear (but hazardous) base underlying, and we set the silver images on top.

## Renounce and recuperate

Capel Cure stepped away from photography in 1860. He died with the tree explosives in 1896, just two years before the first patent was awarded for the next new thing in the evolution of photography: film stock made of nitrocellulose, for which a fibrous, cellulose base is treated to become what's known as celluloid. The benefit of this nitrate film, as it's also known, was its physical flexibility, which allowed it to be used for motion picture filming and projection. The drawback was its propensity to burst into unquenchable flames; this explains its replacement, by the mid-twentieth century, by safer substances. If only Capel Cure had held out a little longer, stayed with the art form and hadn't exploded, he could have used this new technology of vision. Either for filmmaking or for fire-starting; it would have been useful for both.

Although, by the time the first flickers of nitrate film were emerging, Capel Cure had lost his interest in photography. He just gave up on his hobby, it seems. He's not the only one. His contemporary Roger Fenton, the most famous by far of the Crimean War photographers, returned to England and in 1862 stunned the world of photography by giving it all up, selling his equipment, and returning to work in law, until his death seven years later. Perhaps financial pressures had an influence, or maybe the practice of photography, poised between science, art, industry, trade, was uncongenial to him.

## It's a dark world we live in

It's not hard to imagine that taking photos of war, of visible, terrible violence, might affect the photographer. It's not just the proximity to death and fighting, but something about the disparity of this creative activity, in the midst of destruction.

But I speculate, was there something about Crimea, in particular, that prompted these two to renounce? Both Fenton and Capel Cure were there after the excessively dreadful opening year of the war (my history of it [Christopher Hibbert's eye-watering *The Destruction of Lord Raglan*, Pelican, 1961] notes that some of the allied soldiers made huts out of the thigh-bones of the dead, as there was nothing else to form shelter from. Supplies that did arrive had no distribution organized, and were just chucked into the harbour. They desperately needed a Container Corporation-esque protective cardboard box distribution system. Everyone died of cholera. It was a mess.) But it's never good in a war zone.

What would be too much? What would cause a photographer to say either, these things that I have seen and done, or, these images that I have created, are too much for me; I will not and I cannot make any more. I'm interested in what it would take for a photographer to renounce their work, what would happen in the delay between making the photos, then later stepping back, saying, I can't do this any more because of the pictures that keep on rising, blossoming to the surface of my mind, in every dark room and in dreams at night. When does it become unsustainable to have near you, or to keep on forming, these pieces of paper that help you to carry the past around into the future, these little vehicles for something you saw?

## The calming trees

Some photographers leave the zone permanently. Others take time to recover somewhat, to make images of less violent subjects. You can see this in the work of the two late-twentieth-century photographers I mentioned previously. Michael Light doesn't directly say, that I can see, that he needed a calmer project after his *Black Bravo* work, which involved diving in extremely inhospitable, dangerous conditions round places where people had inflicted almost inconceivable damage, to the land and to other people. But it seems that way: in 2017 he went local, doing a small, experimental project for the Palo Alto Art Center, using multi-perspective drone photography fed into data visualization software, creating images of a huge, gentle tree in Rinconada Park, which is where I learned to ride my bike. He shows the branches like a neural network, a path of lights. Critic Maria Porges (in a review in the website *squarecylinder*, 2017) describes his two resulting pictures, of the tree from the top and from side-on, thus: "Both are sheer magic: skeins of light describing the shapes of branches and leaves as cobwebs or jellyfish—microorganisms or nebulae from some distant galaxy."

I like that when Light was representing the moon and then explosions, I kept seeing jellyfish and seaweeds. Then even when he's picturing trees, Porges also sees the jellyfish. And when Light was in fact in the water, when he thought he would be making a film of wreckage and darkness, he got sharks nosing into the picture anyway. There are always animals creeping into the system, nosing in round the edges, getting mixed up along with the other substances, the nitro, seaweed, guano.

## Mariposas

Emmet Gowin was more explicit about wanting to find a recuperative task, after his Nevada Test Site photos, his images of the scarred ground, the human damage. He followed this project with one that was much more soothing, when he went to look for moths in the Central American jungles. The expedition resulted in a book, *Mariposas Nocturnas* (Princeton University Press, 2017. The title is the Spanish name for "night butterflies," or, moths). He took pictures of the moths by day, showing their colours, disguises, and patterns. Sometimes he placed them on books, or, more accurately, waited for them to land on books he had with him—medical manuals, for example, showing Civil War injuries—then photographed them. Then at night he illuminated them and photographed the trails that they made as they moved, the routes and journeys of the creatures in the dark.

What do the scales on the wings of butterflies and moths do? They diffract, filter, adjust the light. For a philosopher like Roger Callois, they prompt musings on mimicry, magic, and madness. For the human and photographer, the optical tools on the wings make beautiful pictures. For Gowin, they help him to restore his equilibrium, regain his sense of how he can be, in the world. They put him back in the picture. In functional terms, the scales and the patterns that they make attract mates and repel predators, camouflage the creature, terrify prey. If the eyes of the butterflies, as the optical biologist Michael Land discovered, are complex telescopes, perhaps they are in complementary evolutionary response to what they are seeing: the scales on the wings might reflect and process the light in a way that is received, appreciated by the eyes of the moths that see the wings. The viewed and the viewer in an optical set-up, like the shark and the scientist. Always doubles, looking and looked-at.

## We shall new shadows make the other way

Capel Cure's strange picture of *My Beasts* has just such moths, in what—a pre-empting of the trauma that he's later going to experience in Crimea? Just a funny picture of one of his hobbies? A still life, a work in the tradition of the painting of the cabinet of curiosities? An exercise, as he gets used to working in the new medium? I don't know; I can't yet decode. I like the way that we (or MoMA) only have this work as a negative, and of course the function of the negative is that you can make a positive print from it. But no-one appears to have done so. Actually, I don't think it could be done now, given the age and state of the negative. (Not concretely done; with image manipulation, of course, you can do anything.) But really, in the flesh, it would be too delicate, too prone to crumble into dust, break down as we try to look at it more directly. So the image stays as a negative, like Michael Light's underwater sharks, like the photogram of the shark egg case. We're still waiting, in one of the pauses that photography offers us, this one between the making of the negative and its positive, right-way-round, more easily understood print. Photography offers many such pauses, gaps, delays, and voids.

I like the moment of latency, when something's there, underlying, but is not yet apparent. It makes me develop a picture in my mind of Capel Cure, marching through his flowering meadow in July, under the summer sky. Sunlight glinting off the butterfly wings. A few shapes of shifting white in the deep blue above him, forming tentacles, airy disks, brief pictures. He's off to the riverbank, just the edge of the water, down to blast the roots of trees with his algae-stabilized dynamite. His leg is giving him some trouble. He's remembering all that waiting, hanging round crumbling churchyards with his uncle and timing the exposures. Maybe he has forgotten how they did things back in Crimea, how they'd blown up the redans, blown up his men. Or maybe that's what distracts him, thinking about *ereipiois*: about fallen buildings, wrecked soldiers, blasted trees. Maybe he is just enjoying the flowers blooming, *anthoun*. It doesn't look like he is paying close enough attention to the matter in hand. Then the same thing happens again.

## Tangled up in blue

We keep seeing the occurrence: the flowers, the explosion, the photos. The scene repeated every damn time, through stories, history, in many people's lives. This is what I am interested in, in literature: the way that we're not looking for the novel (nor The Novel) and exciting, but trying to enjoy or endure this present iteration. It'll always be coming back, but how do I experience it now, in this particular expanse of waiting and delay, in this field of flower meadows or field of vision? It's happened before, and in time it will happen again, but there's something now that touches me, swooping past and leaving a scar that I'll show to the journalists fifty years hence. It'll be there forever, you know. Until suddenly it's not: the person has gone. But will there be traces to remind us?: photos, and tattoos, and faint blue marks from the decaying silver over the bones. All these things we'll find by digging down, back into the past; these things that we'll find, in time.

Sometimes the items have slipped, reshuffled into the wrong layer, and we are confused as to why parts from different zones appear together. Patrolman Len Hendricks taking the disembodied hands, for example, alongside Georg Braun's strange image of lobsterly friendship. Or Capel Cure's image of the bat above the box, with the seaweed, appearing so early in his oeuvre, before he's gone out to the war and explosions, before we might expect any demons returning to plague him, lurking in the unfinished zone.

Time doesn't always go straight. Like light, bending through the medium of different density, it smears. And sometimes we can cut straight through it, like Woolley does in the desert at Ur, sinking a shaft through all the layers, letting us compare, look forwards, look back. We can line up the different strata of images from the past, see who's admiring the blue-silver chemical shadows, who's forming the images in silver markings that allow us to go on. And meanwhile, this is where we live, the latent time.

These prefixes—proto, phyto, photo, nitro—with their meanings and compounds, are useful for thinking about the issues. You just mix them together in the right proportions, the flowers, images, repetitions from the first, the chemical systems, and then, boom, they're gone. Just an empty meadow, blasted trees, some images that don't fade away but carry on looking us straight in the face. After the wooden boxes have had their effect, we're left with the open blue space of the sea, with wrack and traces of silver shining over it. And we're waiting, in all the photographic delay and latency. Waiting for something that's coming up again from below, just ready to flower.

Sculpture of nitrocellulose lacquer on laminated plastic, *"There are five revolutions that must take place either . . ."* Karl Gerstner, Switzerland, 1973.

This was the artwork commissioned from artist and typographer Gerstner for the *Great Ideas of Western Man* series, to accompany an extract from Jean-François Revel's *Without Marx or Jesus*.

# Image Credits

p. 5

William Henry Fox Talbot, [*Hornbeam Leaf*], photogenic drawing negative, 1840.

11.6 cm x 14.9 cm. The J. Paul Getty Museum, Los Angeles. Digital image courtesy of Getty's Open Content Program.

For the wonderful *William Henry Fox Talbot Catalogue Raisonné*, a listing of more than 20,000 paper-based prints and negatives, see talbot.bodleian.ox.ac.uk.

p. 19

X-ray of a wax package containing remains of head-dress with gold leaves, gold ribbon, beads and a silver hair-comb decorated with inlaid rosettes, third millennium BC. 9.5 inches x 8 inches. © The Trustees of the British Museum.

For the head-dress as it appears to the naked eye, see the British Museum's Collection online listings. The museum and the Penn Museum have collaborated to present information on their excavations collections at www.ur-online.org.

p. 40

Anna Atkins, *Conferva melagonium* from *Photographs of British Algae: Cyanotype Impressions*, cyanotype, c. 1843–1853. 250 mm x 200 mm. Source: the Rijksmuseum, Amsterdam.

The Rijksmuseum offers a digital version of its images from *British Algae*; the Natural History Museum, London, has an excellent, different version available via its digitised collections.

p. 60

Michael Light, *"The Rinconada Oak" Seen as a Point Cloud, Heritage Tree #2, 75' Tall, 120' Wide and 200 Years Old, Palo Alto, California*, pigment print, © 2017.

40" x 50". Courtesy of Michael Light; thank you. More on Light's work at www.michaellight.net.

*p. 83*

Abraham Ortelius, page 100r of the *Album Amicorum*, ink on paper (other pages on velum), created over the period c. 1574–1596. 160 mm x 110 mm. With permission of the Master and Fellows of Pembroke College, Cambridge.

The full Ortelius album is available online through the Cambridge Digital Library, at cudl.lib.cam.ac.uk.

*p. 101*

W. J. Johnstone and A. Croall, *Rhodophyllis bifida*, electrotype, plate LXXI of *The Nature-printed British Sea-weeds, volume II, Rhodospermeae*, (London: Bradbury and Evans, 1859, in four volumes). Image from the Biodiversity Heritage Library, of a book held by MBLWHOI Library.

The Biodiversity Heritage Library, at www.biodiversitylibrary.org, has been an invaluable research tool.

*p. 114*

Alfred Capel-Cure, *A Blasted Oak, Hill Hall, 13 May 1858*, albumen silver print. 15.5 cm x 20.6 cm. Image courtesy of: Canadian Centre for Architecture.

*p. 128*

Karl Gerstner, *"There are five revolutions that must take place either. . ."*, pigmented nitrocellulose lacquer on laminated plastic, 1973. 114.3 cm x 113.7 cm x 7.4 cm. Image courtesy of Smithsonian American Art Museum, Gift of Container Corporation of America.

The SAAM has more than three hundred artworks gifted by CCA; browse via americanart.si.edu.

## Acknowledgements

During the time I was writing this book (round spring 2021) I was greatly encouraged and entertained by (at a distance) David Kidd, J. Ed Anderson, and Brixton Tigers, and (in close-up) by Brendan, Ingrid, Lyle, and Lawrence. Thanks for making me laugh.

Thank you to David Collard for forging connections (while foraging collections); to Dr Karen 'Hood for physics; also to Chris McCarthy and Callum McCarthy who haven't had a shout-out before.